NEW
UNDERSTANDING
SCIENCE

1

NEW UNDERSTANDING SCIENCE

1

REVISED

NATIONAL

CURRICULUM

EDITION

JOE
BOYD
St Augustine's High School,
Edinburgh

WALTER
WHITELAW
Advisory Service and Quality
Assurance (Science),Edinburgh

JOHN MURRAY

© Joe Boyd and Walter Whitelaw 1989, 1996

First published 1989
by John Murray (Publishers) Ltd
50 Albemarle Street
London W1X 4BD

Reprinted 1989, 1990, 1991, 1992
This edition 1996

Layouts by Fiona Webb
Cartoons by Ainslie MacLeod
Line drawings by Tom Cross
Natural history drawings by David Webb

Typeset in 11½/13pt Futura Book by Wearset, Boldon,
Tyne and Wear
Printed in Great Britain by Cambus Litho Ltd, East Kilbride, Scotland

A CIP catalogue record for this book is available from the British Library.

ISBN 0-7195-7242-8

Contents

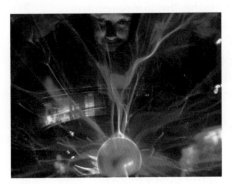

Extensions

Introduction

A How to use this book

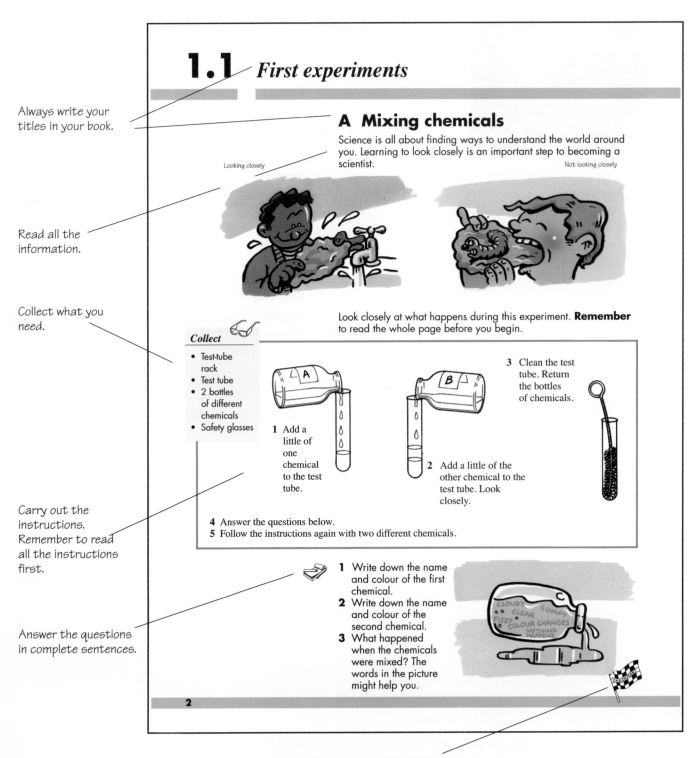

Always write your titles in your book.

1.1 *First experiments*

A Mixing chemicals

Science is all about finding ways to understand the world around you. Learning to look closely is an important step to becoming a scientist.

Looking closely

Not looking closely

Read all the information.

Look closely at what happens during this experiment. **Remember** to read the whole page before you begin.

Collect what you need.

Collect
- Test-tube rack
- Test tube
- 2 bottles of different chemicals
- Safety glasses

1 Add a little of one chemical to the test tube.

2 Add a little of the other chemical to the test tube. Look closely.

3 Clean the test tube. Return the bottles of chemicals.

4 Answer the questions below.
5 Follow the instructions again with two different chemicals.

Carry out the instructions. Remember to read all the instructions first.

1 Write down the name and colour of the first chemical.
2 Write down the name and colour of the second chemical.
3 What happened when the chemicals were mixed? The words in the picture might help you.

Answer the questions in complete sentences.

CLOUDY LUMPY CLEAR FIZZY COLOUR CHANGES NOTHING HAPPENS

2

Complete your learning log (for 1.1) and have your work checked by your teacher, who will tell you what to do next.

B Following instructions

It is important to read and then to follow instructions carefully in science. Sometimes there are a lot of instructions. These need to be done in the right order to make your experiment work.

Collect

- Piece of white paper

1 Write down the time on the upper left-hand corner of the paper.

2 Fold the paper **carefully** in half.

3 Fold the paper again into quarters.

4 Unfold the paper. Write the letters *I* and *A* in the upper left-hand quarter of the page. Use **large** letters and write in your **best** handwriting.

5 Find something in your bag to cover up the letters.

6 Write the letters *D*, *O* and *N* in the bottom left-hand quarter of the paper. Hide these letters with something. Your paper should now look like this.

7 Write the letters *M* and *A* in the top right-hand quarter of the paper.

8 Write the letters *K*, *E* and *Y* in the bottom right-hand quarter of the paper.

9 Remove everything from the paper.

10 Draw a line between the *I* and the first *A*. Draw another line between the *M* and the second *A*.

11 Put your hands on top of your head. Read the hidden message. Say hee-haw, hee-haw!

12 Do not follow instructions 4 to 11.

13 Write the time in the bottom right-hand corner of the paper.

Following Instructions

1
This is science

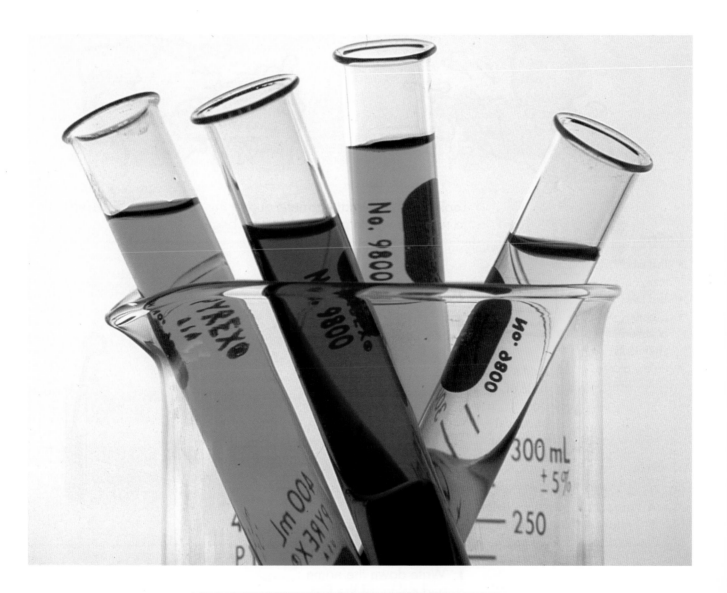

1.1 *First experiments*

A Mixing chemicals

Science is all about finding ways to understand the world around you. Learning to look closely is an important step to becoming a scientist.

Looking closely

Not looking closely

Look closely at what happens during this experiment. **Remember** to read the whole page before you begin.

Collect

- Test-tube rack
- Test tube
- 2 bottles of different chemicals
- Safety glasses

1 Add a little of one chemical to the test tube.

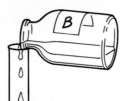

2 Add a little of the other chemical to the test tube. Look closely.

3 Clean the test tube. Return the bottles of chemicals.

4 Answer the questions below.
5 Follow the instructions again with two different chemicals.

1 Write down the name and colour of the first chemical.
2 Write down the name and colour of the second chemical.
3 What happened when the chemicals were mixed? The words in the picture might help you.

B Seeing is believing

The photographs below are of everyday objects. They have been taken from an unusual angle. Look closely at the photograph for hints about the object.

 1 Write down the name of each object.
What was the best hint in each photograph?

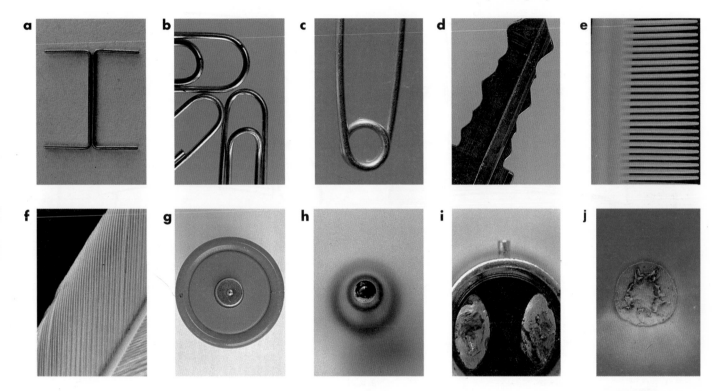

2 Collect a copy of the drawings below and stick it into your book.

What **two** things can you see in each picture?

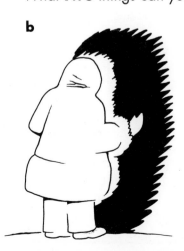

3

1.2 *First reports*

A Junior reporter

A scientist follows instructions and looks closely at what is happening. The good scientist then writes a careful report. Your next task is to practise this skill.

Writing carefully

Writing carelessly

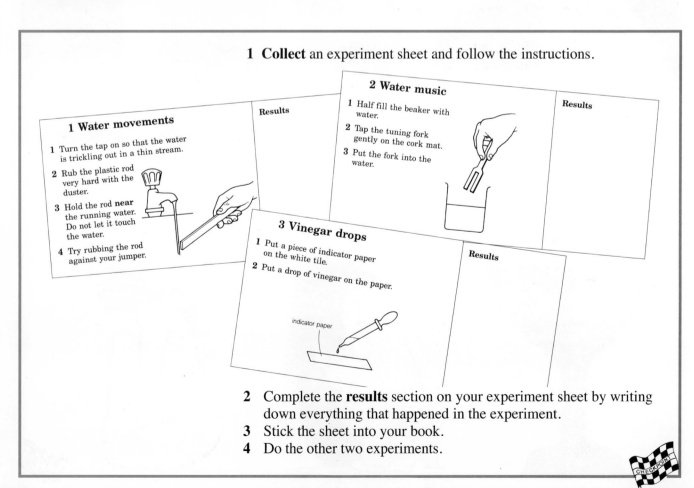

1 Collect an experiment sheet and follow the instructions.

1 Water movements

1 Turn the tap on so that the water is trickling out in a thin stream.

2 Rub the plastic rod very hard with the duster.

3 Hold the rod **near** the running water. Do not let it touch the water.

4 Try rubbing the rod against your jumper.

Results

2 Water music

1 Half fill the beaker with water.

2 Tap the tuning fork gently on the cork mat.

3 Put the fork into the water.

Results

3 Vinegar drops

1 Put a piece of indicator paper on the white tile.

2 Put a drop of vinegar on the paper.

indicator paper

Results

2 Complete the **results** section on your experiment sheet by writing down everything that happened in the experiment.

3 Stick the sheet into your book.

4 Do the other two experiments.

B Ace reporter

Practise your reporting skills by doing these three experiments. Report your results in the same way as before.

4 Watch the birdie

1 Hold the knitting needle between your hands as shown.

2 Rub your hands together backwards and forwards. The needle will twirl.

3 Look at the picture card while you do this.

Results

5 Fizzy veg

1 Add a little clear liquid to a test tube.

2 Put a little chopped potato into the clear liquid.

3 Clean the test tube afterwards.

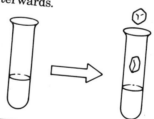

Results

6 Seeing sound

1 Look at the little screen.

2 Put your mouth close to the microphone and make a loud high noise. For example, whistle.

3 Make a low noise now.

Results

1.3 *First measurements*

A Measurement scales

People have always needed to measure quantities like mass, length, time, volume and temperature.

Balance

Body

Hourglass

Bushel

Elbow

These methods of measurement were not very exact. Today we use more accurate instruments.

Balance

Mass (weight) in grams (g)

Metre rule

Length in centimetres (cm)

Clock

Time in seconds (s)

Measuring cylinder

Volume in cubic centimetres (cm^3)

Thermometer

Temperature in degrees Celsius (°C)

You can compare modern and historical measurements of length.
Measure the length of the bench
a in centimetres (with a metre rule)
b in hands (with your hand)
c in hands (with your partner's hand).

= one hand

Record your results in a table.

---

1 Collect and complete a copy of the modern scales diagram.
2 Why is it better to measure with a metre rule rather than a hand?

B Body building

Hamish was famished. He had been trapped on an island for ages. All he could catch was a small and unusual animal. Luckily Hamish was a good scientist. Before he ate this rare animal, he recorded some of its measurements. Here they are.

Part of animal	Measurement
body	mass 20 g
2 front legs	length 6 cm
1 back leg	length 5 cm
head	volume 10 cm^3
tail	length 8 cm
nose	mass 2 g

Make an accurate model of the animal. Your measurements should be the same as those in the table.

Use plasticine for the body, the head and the nose. Use straws for the legs. Use string for the tail. Put a smile on the face of the animal.

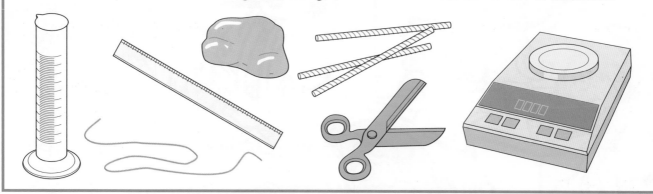

1 Draw an accurate picture of your animal.
2 Measure and record on your drawing
   a the length of the body
   b the height from the ground to the top of its head
   c the total mass of the animal.

1.4 *Safety first*

A Classroom sense

1 Scientists work safely. Look at the picture below.
Collect a copy and stick it into your book.
2 Put a red ring round each danger in the cartoon. Number each one. There are at least ten dangers.
3 Work with a partner. Make up and write down a safety rule to control five of the dangers in the cartoon.

Collect a list of safety rules. Keep them safe!

B Filling time

You are going to practise three simple scientific skills that you will use often. It is important to think about safety even when you do simple things.

Collect

- Small beaker of water
- Dropper
- Dimple tile

1 Use the dropper to fill one of the dimples to the brim.
2 If you spill any water or overfill the dimple, try again.

Collect

- Sample tube
- Black paper
- Spatula
- Bottle of salt

1 The sample tube has a mark on it. Put the sample tube on the black paper.
2 Use the spatula to fill the sample tube up to the mark with salt. If you spill any salt on the black paper start again.

Collect

- Test tube
- Test tube rack
- Spatula
- Dropper
- Bottle of acid
- Bottle of green powder
- Safety glasses

1 The test tube has two marks on it. Fill it to the first mark with the green powder.
2 Add acid up to the second mark.
3 Mix the powder and the acid safely like this.
4 Watch (and feel) what happens.

1 Why should you not spill chemicals?
2 Why should you never mix chemicals in a test tube by turning the test tube upside down with your thumb on the top?
3 Write a short report to describe what happened in the final experiment.

1.5 *Think!*

A Conduct a survey

Scientists gather and use evidence to help them understand things. You have to gather evidence about **one** of these topics. Ask people in your school for their opinions on:

Fast foods

Educational TV programmes

Exercise

Your group have to design and use a survey. You then have to think about what your results mean. Your survey form could be like the one below.

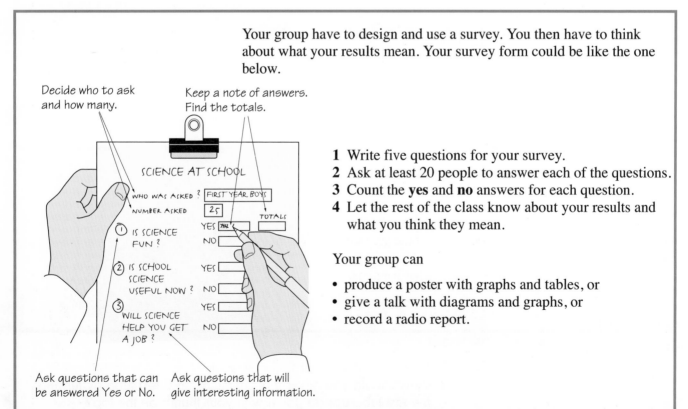

Decide who to ask and how many.

Keep a note of answers. Find the totals.

SCIENCE AT SCHOOL

WHO WAS ASKED ? FIRST YEAR BOYS

NUMBER ASKED 25

TOTALS

① IS SCIENCE FUN ? YES NO

② IS SCHOOL SCIENCE USEFUL NOW ? YES NO

③ WILL SCIENCE HELP YOU GET A JOB ? YES NO

Ask questions that can be answered Yes or No.

Ask questions that will give interesting information.

1 Write five questions for your survey.
2 Ask at least 20 people to answer each of the questions.
3 Count the **yes** and **no** answers for each question.
4 Let the rest of the class know about your results and what you think they mean.

Your group can

- produce a poster with graphs and tables, or
- give a talk with diagrams and graphs, or
- record a radio report.

B Survey evidence

1 Write down what you learn about each topic (a–d) from the evidence in the graph.

2 Explain which graph you would trust
  a most **b** least.

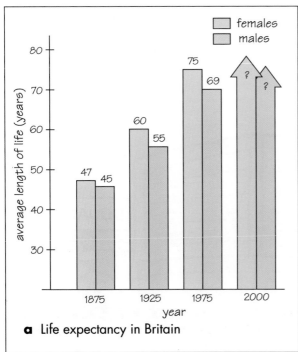

a Life expectancy in Britain

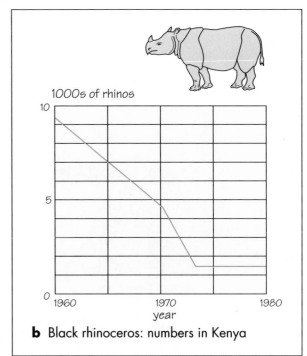

b Black rhinoceros: numbers in Kenya

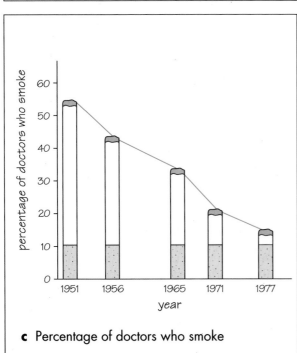

c Percentage of doctors who smoke

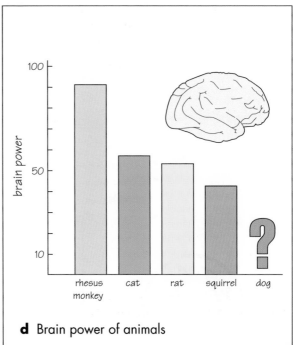

d Brain power of animals

1.6 *Problem*

Design a sign

Your problem is to design labels for a shipment of dangerous chemicals. The chemicals are being delivered to a foreign country where nobody speaks English. There are three kinds of chemicals in the shipment

- **Flammable**—these will catch fire easily
- **Poisonous**—these will kill
- **Explosive**—these could explode.

Collect

- Design sheet
- Coloured pencils

Here are some things to think about:
    Your label will have to go on a bottle.
    Should your label • be coloured?
                      • have words?
                      • be complicated?

Now solve the problem.
Draw your three labels on the design sheet and stick them in your book.

Ask your partner what he or she thinks of your labels. Ask him or her to write in the comment box on your sheet.

1.7 *Talkabout*

Life in the future

How do you think science and technology will have changed the world by the time you are 50 years old?

School

Travel

Fashion

Homes

1.8 *Readabout*

Alfred Nobel

Alfred Nobel was born in Sweden in 1833. He was a scientist and a businessman. In 1866 he invented dynamite and later on he discovered other explosives that were even more powerful. He then set up factories to make his explosives and became very rich indeed.

Alfred Nobel was worried that his inventions might be misused. He wanted to encourage people to work for the good of humanity. He decided to set up a fund to award prizes for the very best work in science, medicine, literature and peace. Nobel died in 1896 and the first Nobel Prizes were awarded in 1901.

Today most research scientists dream of the honour of receiving a Nobel Prize. Perhaps one of you will produce work that Alfred Nobel would have wanted to reward!

1 Copy and complete the personal history file about Alfred Nobel.

> Name: _____
>
> Place of birth: _____
>
> Year of birth: _____
>
> Three interesting facts:
>
> _____
>
> _____
>
> _____

2 Use the books in the classroom or books from a library to find out more about Nobel and his work. Write a paragraph about what you find out. The key words to look up in the index are **Nobel, Nobel Prize, dynamite**.

2
Solutions

1 Problems can be solved by using your existing knowledge and understanding.
2 A substance dissolves by a different amount
   a in different solvents   and   **b** at different temperatures.
3 Mixtures can be separated by using methods like chromatography, filtration and distillation.

2.1 *Water movements*

A Dry up

Water has different forms: **frozen** water (a solid), **liquid** water and water **vapour** (a gas).

Liquid water changes into water vapour when it gains heat. A change like this is called **evaporation**.

Water vapour changes back into liquid water when it loses heat and cools. This kind of change is called **condensation**.

A puddle on the road disappears because the water evaporates. The water will evaporate more quickly on a hot or a windy day and when the water is spread out. Use these key ideas to solve the following problem as quickly as you can.

There's always a key to unlock any problem

Problem

The last paper towel in the universe has fallen in a puddle. You have to dry the towel out as quickly as possible. You also have to complete a report sheet saying how you did this.

Your teacher will write down the time when you collect the wet paper towel. Timing will stop when you hand in the dry towel **and** a complete report.

Hints

- Talk about the problem with your partner.
- Plan your work before you collect the wet towel. Remember that timing starts when you collect it.
- Fill in as much of the report as you can before you start. This will save time.
- **Collect** any equipment you need **before** you collect the wet towel.
- Don't copy other people's ideas. They are probably not as good as your own.

Now solve the problem.

B Rain down

It rains somewhere in Britain almost every day. It rains because liquid water is evaporating slowly all the time. The gas rises into the air and cools. When it loses enough heat it condenses.

Collect

- 'Water board'
- Word cards

1 Use the picture above to describe the journey of a raindrop. Include words like **liquid**, **condense**, **evaporate slowly** and **gas** in your answer.

2 Water also **freezes** and **melts**. Place the word cards on the 'water board' in the correct places. Copy the completed board into your book.

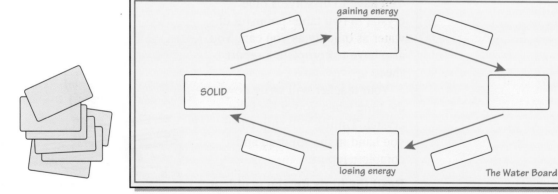

gaining energy

SOLID

losing energy

The Water Board

3 **Collect** a copy of the picture below. Stick it into your book. Write the word which describes what is happening to the water in each picture.

a   b   c   d   e

2.2 *Changing appearances*

A Dissolving

Water is wonderful stuff. It can make things seem to disappear. Salt seems to disappear into water. So does sugar. This disappearing act is known as **dissolving**.

A substance that dissolves is **soluble**.

The substance that does the dissolving is a **solvent**.

Together, the solvent and the soluble substance make a **solution**.

Another problem-solving competition

You have to dissolve a blue crystal in two tablespoonsful of water as quickly as you can. You also have to complete a report sheet.

Your teacher will write down the time when you collect the crystal. Timing will stop when you hand in the solution and a complete report.

Read the hints for the problem on page 16.
Now solve the problem.

Don't dive in. Discuss the key to the problem with your partner first.

Collect

- Set of substances
- Test-tube rack
- Test tube
- Wooden splint
- Two solvents

Water is not the only solvent.
1 Use one chemical substance and one solvent at a time.
2 Add a small amount of substance to a test tube half full of solvent.
   Use just enough substance to cover the end of a wooden splint.
3 Shake the tube gently from side to side.
4 Decide if the substance is soluble or insoluble in the solvent.

1 Put your results in a table like this.

Solvent	Substance	Soluble or insoluble
ethanol	iron oxide	insoluble

2 Your teacher may show you that a gas can also be soluble.

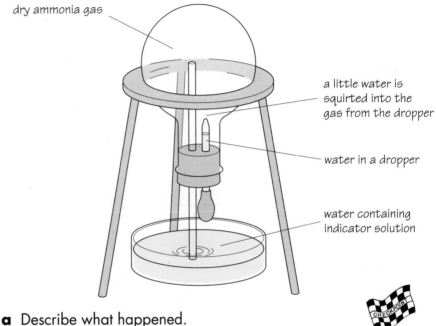

dry ammonia gas

a little water is squirted into the gas from the dropper

water in a dropper

water containing indicator solution

a Describe what happened.
b Is ammonia gas soluble or insoluble in water?

B Testing ideas

Decide which of the phrases is about **melting** and which is about **dissolving**. (You can use a phrase twice.) Write down the words 'melting' and 'dissolving' followed by all their phrases.

Phrases

| needs heat | one substance | two substances | doesn't need heat |

| needs water | needs a solid | makes a liquid | doesn't need water |

2.3 *Changing the temperature*

A Crystal clear

A solvent can get filled up with dissolved substance. The solution is **saturated** when no more of the substance can dissolve in the solvent.

A different amount of substance can be dissolved in the solvent if the temperature is changed.

Collect

- Microscope
- Slide
- Cover slip
- Dropper

1 Your teacher will show you how to set up the microscope. Focus it carefully.

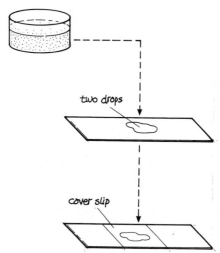

two drops

cover slip

2 Take your slide and dropper to the hot saturated solution. Put two drops of the solution on the slide. Leave it on your bench for one minute. It will cool and some water will evaporate.

3 Cover the drops with the cover slip.
4 Look at the slide under low-power magnification. Be patient. Wait for several minutes.

1 Describe what you did.
2 Make a large drawing of what you saw. (Draw the correct shape.)
3 Use the pictures and words below to **explain** what you saw.

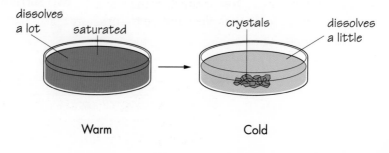

dissolves a lot   saturated   crystals   dissolves a little

Warm   Cold

Volcano

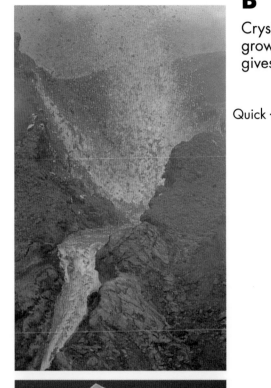

Large crystals

B Grow slow

Crystals which grow slowly are usually bigger than crystals which grow quickly. Quick cooling gives small crystals. Slow evaporation gives big crystals.

Small crystals

Quick ⟶

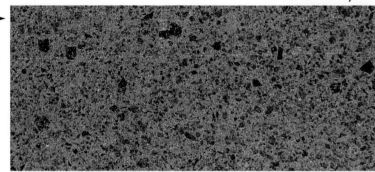

⟵ Slow

Salt flats

Collect

- Bottle of alum
- Test tube
- Test-tube rack
- Wooden splint

You have to grow a huge crystal of alum from half a test tube full of water. The size of your crystal will be compared with the others in your class.

When you plan, think about
- the sentences at the top of this page
- the starting temperature of the water
- what to do with the solution to form large crystals.

Discuss your ideas with your teacher, then start growing!

1 Describe what you did to grow the crystal.
2 Draw a diagram and label it to explain why the crystal grew.
3 Who grew the biggest crystal in the class? How did you decide this crystal was the biggest?

2.4 *Colourful papers*

A The great ink stink

Materials often contain different substances which are mixed together. **Chromatography** is a way of separating some mixtures like inks or dyes. One method is shown below.

Collect

- Filter paper
- Felt pens
- Beaker

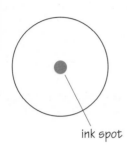

ink spot

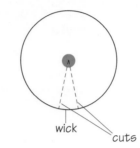

wick
cuts

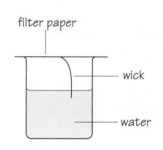

filter paper
wick
water

1 Make a spot in the centre of a filter paper.

2 Cut the paper as shown.

3 Bend the cut piece downwards. This is the wick. Lay the filter paper on top of a beaker of water and dip the wick into the water. Wait.

Collect

- Card with message
- Any equipment you need

Your problem is to discover who sent you a cheeky birthday card. Here are the suspects.

AUNTY DOTE

UNCLE CARBUNCLE

COUSIN FUSSIN

YA BOO GET BACK TO THE ZOO

You have a pen from each suspect and some ink from the card. Use chromatography to discover the culprit.

Discuss • how to remove a sample of ink from the card
• how to compare this ink with suspects' pens.

Now solve the problem.

Write a report about your experiment. Your earlier problem report sheets will show you what to include. Stick the filter papers with your results into your book.

B Be a smartie

Foods are often coloured by adding a dye. The dye could be a single substance on its own or a mixture of coloured substances.

Collect

- Spotting tile
- Filter paper
- Smartie (dark colour)
- Small paint brush
- Evaporating dish
- Dropper

1 Put the Smartie on the tile and add **three** drops of water.
2 Brush the Smartie until the dye has dissolved in the water.
3 Use the chromatography method to find out if the dye is a single substance or a mixture of substances.

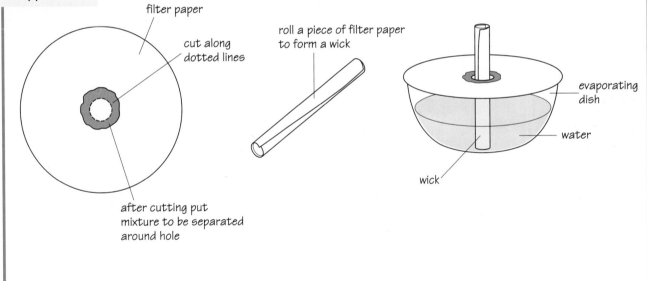

filter paper

cut along dotted lines

roll a piece of filter paper to form a wick

evaporating dish

water

wick

after cutting put mixture to be separated around hole

1 Write a report about the experiment. Your earlier problem report sheets will show you what to include.
2 Write the dye colour on your filter paper and stick it on to the class poster.
3 Using the class poster make two lists
   a dyes which are single substances
   b dyes which are mixtures of substances.

2.5 *Fix the mix*

A Salt from rock

There are several methods of separating mixtures.

• **Filtering**—e.g. separating **sand** and **water**.

Sand is insoluble in water. It is caught by the filter paper. The water goes straight through.

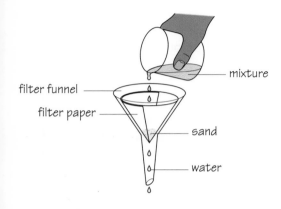

filter funnel
filter paper
mixture
sand
water

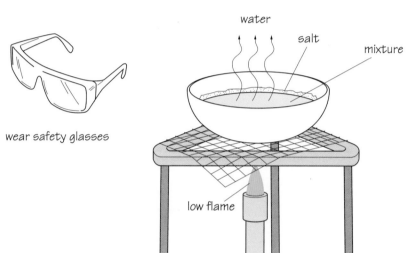

wear safety glasses

water
salt
mixture
low flame

• **Making crystals**—e.g. separating **salt** from **salty water**.

Salt is soluble in water. As the water evaporates, the salt is left behind in the form of crystals.

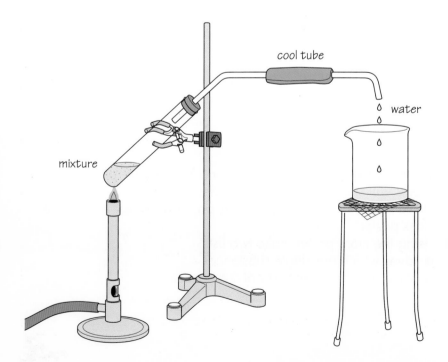

cool tube
water
mixture

• **Distillation**—e.g. separating **water** from **salty water**.

Salt is soluble in water. The water evaporates and goes through the tube. It is cooled in the tube and condenses back into water.

Rock salt is salt from the ground. The salt is mixed with dirt and bits of rock. Your problem is to clean up the salt so that it is good enough to eat.

You will be given about 5g of rock salt.

You have to produce as much clean dry salt from it as you can. You will be judged on

- time taken
- weight of salt
- whiteness of salt.

You can use any method or methods to separate the salt from the rock and dirt. You should only need basic laboratory equipment.

 Write a full report about your experiment.

B Separating quiz

Collect a copy of the pictures below. Name the method of separating mixtures which you would use to solve each of the problems.

1 Waiter, there's glass in my soup.

2 Waiter, water everywhere and not a drop to drink.

3 Waiter, all the sugar's dissolved in the wet bowl.

4 There's mud in the drinking water.

5 Which blue car has bumped into mine?

2.6 *Problem*

Scottish spring water

Find the minerals

Rocks are usually mixtures of different substances. The solid substances in the mixture are called minerals. When water flows over and through rock it will dissolve some of the minerals.

Composition of Highland Spring water

Hot spring in Yellowstone Park, USA

Component	mg/l
calcium	392
magnesium	54
sodium	174
potassium	16
carbonate	216
chloride	276
sulphate	1021
nitrate	< 0.0002
fluoride	2
iron	0.009
aluminium	0.0005
total dissolved solids at 180°C	2120

Composition of mineral water from hot spring at Bath

Collect

- Mineral water
- Photocopy of label
- The equipment you need

Your problem is to design a way to show that mineral water contains dissolved substances.

Hints

- The amount of minerals dissolved in the water may be very small.
- Your teacher can help you if you get stuck.

1 Stick the mineral water label into your book.
2 Describe how you solved the problem.
3 Would you expect water from hot springs to contain more or less dissolved material than water from cold pools? Explain your answer.

2.7 *Talkabout*

Living underwater

Imagine you had to live underwater. What problems would you have to solve? How would you solve them?

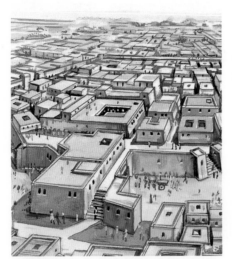

Mohenjo Daro

Rome

Keep it clean

When people in the ancient world began to live closer together in towns and cities they had new problems to solve. One of these was how to avoid sickness and disease. If dirty water and human waste are left lying around there is a great danger of typhoid and cholera. These diseases are deadly and spread quickly through a town.

The first place known to have a sewage system was Mohenjo Daro. This great city was carefully planned 4,500 years ago. It was built on a huge mound of earth and stones above the flood plain of the River Indus, in what we now call Pakistan.

Every house had a bathroom and toilet. Earthenware pipes drained water and waste from the houses into larger pipes that ran under the streets. People solved the problem of blocked drains too. Manhole covers let cleaners into the pipes to clear the system. The sewage was piped to fields on the outskirts of the city.

Other civilisations developed sanitation systems too. The Romans built drains in Rome 2,500 years ago. They built a main drainage pipe between the centre of the city and the River Tigris that is still used today.

Every home in the Inca city of Cuzco (Peru) had stone drains 1,000 years ago. Water from mountain streams washed through these, taking waste away from the city.

The Ashanti kingdom in West Africa 200 years ago had a water drainage system in its main buildings. The pipes carried the waste to a nearby river and they were cleaned out with boiling water every day. Every small village had its own public toilet.

However, in most of the great cities of Europe, sewage systems were unknown until the end of the nineteenth century – about 100 years ago. Then sewage was carried by pipes to local rivers. Most of these drains are still in use today.

1 Draw a timeline showing examples of sewage systems in 5 different civilisations. On the timeline write

   • when the system was used
   • where the system was developed
   • how the system worked.

2 Use books in the classroom or from a library to find out more about drainage and sewage systems. Key words to look up in the index are **sanitation**, **sewage**, **sewer.**

3
Look alive

Fig 3.1

BIG IDEAS IN THIS UNIT

1 There are seven pieces of evidence that things are alive.
2 All animals and all plants can be classified into groups.
3 You are a vertebrate and a mammal.
4 A key can be used to name an unknown animal or plant.

3.1 *The set of living things*

A What living things do

You belong to the most important set of things on the earth. You belong to the set of **living things**. So do seeds, eggs, mushrooms, trees and insects. Living things do what non-living things cannot do on their own.

Each cartoon hints at **one** thing which only living things can do. Look carefully at the cartoons. Discuss each one with your partner.

A DAY IN THE LIFE OF **SQUEAKY the MOUSE.**

1 My birthday

2 A breath of fresh air before lunch, then...

3 ... measure up for a new suit.

4 Greens for lunch. I won't leaf any!

5 Go across the road to visit my friend.

6 Help!

7 What a relief! Phew!

 Copy and complete this table.

Cartoon	What the living thing is doing
1	
2	
3	
4	
5	
6	
7	

B Observing a living thing

Collect

* A living thing

Care

You are now going to search for evidence of life.

Remember, living things deserve to be treated with care and respect at all times. **Do not harm them.**

Always complete the study of one living thing before you go on to another.

hop
wriggle
swim
bend

bigger
changes
slow

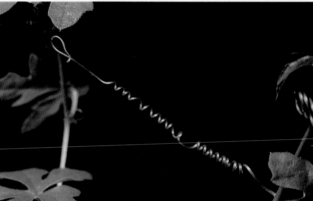

chomp
chew
catch
collect
trap

bubbles
condensation
pant
waste

Write a paragraph about your observations. Also **explain** how you know that the creature is alive. The words on this page will help you to spot and write about important evidence. Always include a large drawing of the living thing.

A Be a good looker

People have invented a scientific way of grouping **all** living things. If you observe living things closely you see that some of them are similar. The similarities allow us to classify living things. These similarities are important details for a scientific observer.

The scientist puts all animals into two main groups. The important detail is a **backbone**. Animals with a backbone are called **vertebrates**. Animals without a backbone are called **invertebrates**.

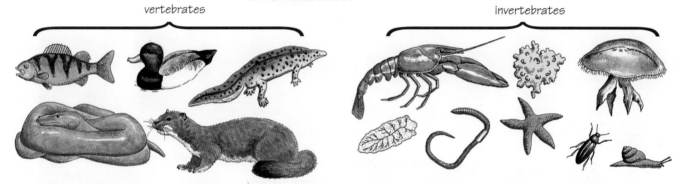

vertebrates   invertebrates

Plants are also classified into groups by identifying important details. The important details are **flowers** and **seeds**. Plants can be divided into two groups, **flowering** (seed-carrying) plants and **non-flowering** (seedless) plants.

flowering plants   non-flowering plants

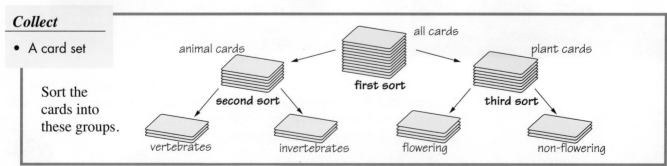

Collect

• A card set

Sort the cards into these groups.

all cards
animal cards   plant cards
first sort
second sort   **third sort**
vertebrates   invertebrates   flowering   non-flowering

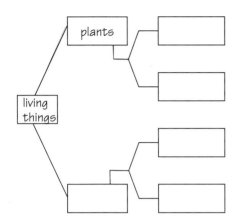

1 Imagine you had one card for *each and every* living thing on Earth. Copy and complete the sorting diagram to show how you would sort all these cards into groups.

2 **a** What is the difference between the two groups of animals?
  b Why is it sometimes difficult to spot this important detail?

3 **a** What is the difference between the two groups of plants?
  b Why is it sometimes difficult to spot this important detail?

B Set and match

1 Look at the three sets below.
  a Which set contains four vertebrates?
  b Which sets contain four invertebrates?
  c Which animal is the odd one out in each set?

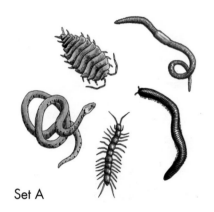

Set A

Set B

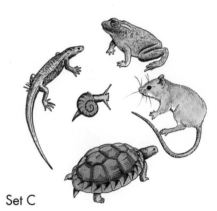

Set C

2 Look at the plant sets below.
  a Which set contains three flowering plants?
  b What does the other set contain?
  c Which plant is the odd one out in each set?

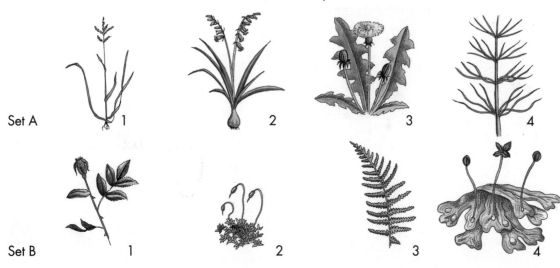

Set A   1   2   3   4

Set B   1   2   3   4

3.3 *Who is spineless?*

A Groups of vertebrates

The skill of looking closely at something to find the important details can help you to understand the scientific way of putting animals into groups.

1 Work with a partner. Shuffle the cards.
2 Sort the cards into these five different groups (or **classes**) of **vertebrates**.

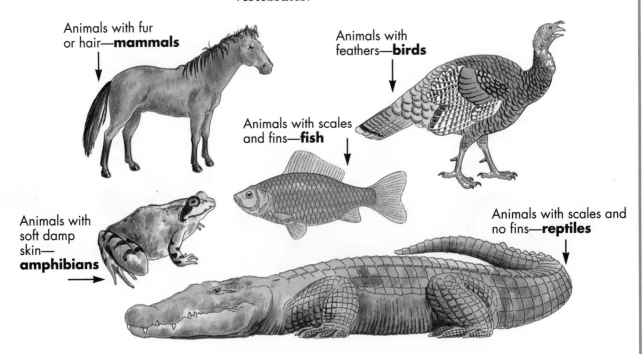

Animals with fur or hair—**mammals**

Animals with feathers—**birds**

Animals with scales and fins—**fish**

Animals with scales and no fins—**reptiles**

Animals with soft damp skin—**amphibians**

3 Once you and your partner are sure of these classes, show them to your teacher. You must know these classes very well to be able to win the following game.
4 Now play the game (the rules are given on the left).

Rules

* Play 'Snap' in the usual way, but more quietly!
* If the top two cards on the pile are from the same vertebrate class then whisper 'Snap'.
* Use the five vertebrate classes: fish, birds, mammals, amphibians, reptiles.

 When you have finished, copy and complete the table. Use your five card classes of vertebrates to help you.

Vertebrate class	Example	Body covering	Warm/cold-blooded	Eggs or live birth	Suckles young	Limbs
1 mammals	stoat	furry/hairy	warm-blooded			
2						
3						
4						
5						

B Using vertebrate classes

Look at these animals.

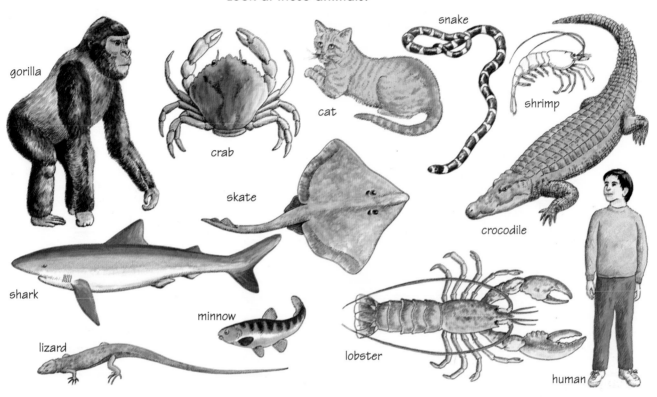

gorilla
crab
cat
snake
shrimp
skate
crocodile
shark
minnow
lizard
lobster
human

1 Divide the animals into four sets. Give each set a name and **write** the members of each set in your book. **Explain** why one set is the odd one out.

2 A hawk and a penguin look very different. Yet both are members of the class of **birds**. This means that they are similar in some important details. **Write** down these important details.

hawk

penguin

Collect

• Pack of cards

Happy Families

1 Deal all the cards out. (There should be at least three players.)

2 Try to collect a complete set—a **Happy Family**.

3 The player on the dealer's left begins by asking one of the other players for a card. She or he must name the class wanted and also identify the important detail on the card. For example, 'Please give me the mammal card with live birth'.

4 If the player gets the card then she or he has another turn. If not, then the next player has their turn.

3.4 *The door to identification*

A Using keys

A scientist can identify an unknown object, such as a rock or an animal, by using a **key**. A key is easy to use. See if you can work this one out.

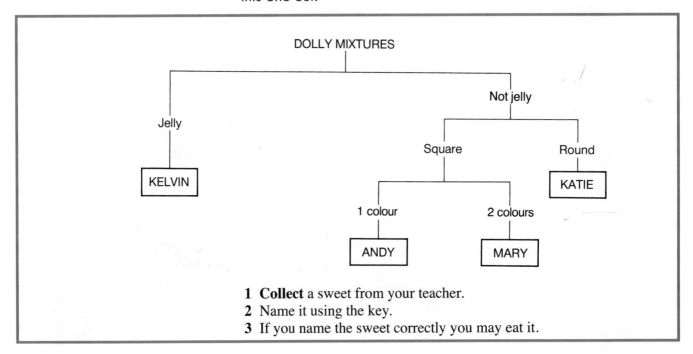

DOLLY MIXTURES
- Jelly → KELVIN
- Not jelly
  - Square
    - 1 colour → ANDY
    - 2 colours → MARY
  - Round → KATIE

1 **Collect** a sweet from your teacher.
2 Name it using the key.
3 If you name the sweet correctly you may eat it.

1 Describe how you used the key to name your sweet.
2 Use the key below to name these pond animals. Write the answers in your book.

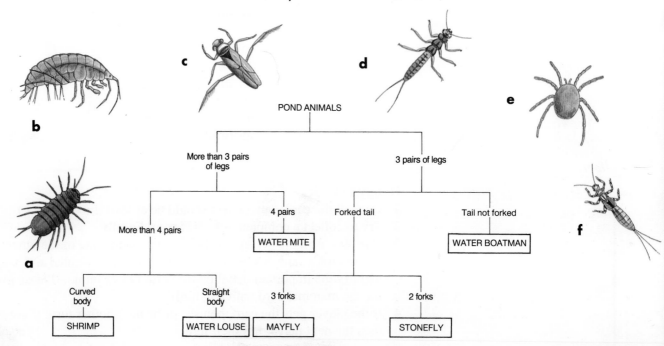

POND ANIMALS
- More than 3 pairs of legs
  - More than 4 pairs
    - Curved body → SHRIMP
    - Straight body → WATER LOUSE
  - 4 pairs → WATER MITE
- 3 pairs of legs
  - Forked tail
    - 3 forks → MAYFLY
    - 2 forks → STONEFLY
  - Tail not forked → WATER BOATMAN

a
b
c
d
e
f

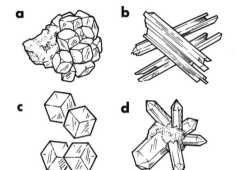

a b

c d

3 Use this key to name these crystals. Write the answers in your book.

Key for crystals
1 Long needle-like crystals   Go to 2
    Block-like crystals   Go to 3
2 Pencil-like ends with six sides **Quartz**
    Sliced ends with flat face   **Potassium nitrate**
3 Cube with sharp corners   **Common salt**
    Cube with sliced corners   **Galena**

B Key practice

1 Use the key to name these birds. Write the answers in your book.

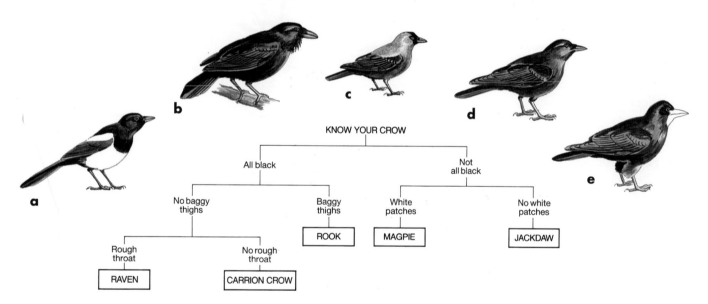

KNOW YOUR CROW

All black   Not all black

No baggy thighs   Baggy thighs   White patches   No white patches

ROOK   MAGPIE   JACKDAW

Rough throat   No rough throat

RAVEN   CARRION CROW

a b c d e

2 Use the key to name each scientist. Write the answers in your book.

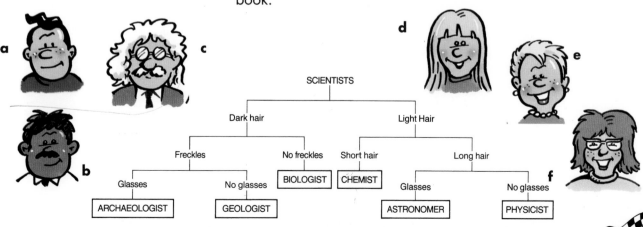

SCIENTISTS

Dark hair   Light Hair

Freckles   No freckles   Short hair   Long hair

Glasses   No glasses   BIOLOGIST   CHEMIST   Glasses   No glasses

ARCHAEOLOGIST   GEOLOGIST   ASTRONOMER   PHYSICIST

a b c d e f

3.5 *Problem*

House a louse

Your problem is to help Sneaky the woodlouse find a pleasant home.

Collect

- Dish with a woodlouse in it
- Empty dish
- Filter papers
- Beaker of water
- Sandpaper
- Black paper

Hints: collect evidence about Sneaky's behaviour

- Does Sneaky like—rough or smooth ground?
  —damp or dry ground?
  —dark or light?
- You need to give Sneaky a choice in the dish. Design a fair test.
- You need to record Sneaky's movements for a short time.

For example,

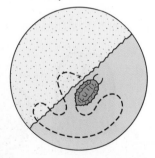
Sneaky's movements

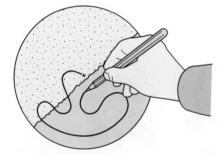
Your record over the time

- You need to repeat an experiment to check your result.

Now solve the problem.

Write a letter to the Housing Department. Tell them what kind of house your friend Sneaky would prefer. They will need some evidence so tell them about your experiments.

3.6 *Talkabout*

Life on other planets

Are there living things on other planets? What might they be like?
How might we discover them?

Charles Darwin

Charles Darwin was born in England in 1809. He was the son of a doctor. When he was about your age, he collected things like postage franks (which are like stamps) and minerals.

In 1831 he volunteered to sail on a survey ship to South America. The voyage was to last five years, and it was the beginning of Charles Darwin's great work.

Whenever the ship stopped, Darwin went ashore in search of interesting animals and plants. He made studies of unusual living things and also of unusual rocks and crystals. He found some very strange animals living on the Galapagos Islands, for example iguanas, which are huge lizards. He also found fourteen different varieties of finches. Each kind had a different beak. Darwin was such a good scientist because he noticed details like this. He closely observed things. He then asked himself questions like

- *Why are some animals so similar and yet they live on islands far away from each other?*
- *Why are some similar animals slightly different from each other?*
- *What causes the differences?*

Darwin sent samples back to Britain so that he could study them in more detail when he returned. He finally worked out how one kind of living thing could change slowly into another kind over a long period of time. This change is called evolution. Darwin wrote a famous book called 'On the Origin of Species by Means of Natural Selection' to explain his ideas. It was a best seller in 1859. Some of his ideas still cause arguments today.

1 Copy and complete the personal history file about Charles Darwin.

> Name: _____
>
> Place of birth: _____
>
> Year of birth: _____
>
> Three interesting facts:
>
> _____
>
> _____
>
> _____

2 Use the books in the classroom or books from a library to find out more about Darwin and his work. Write a paragraph about what you find out. The key words to look up in the index are **Darwin**, **natural selection**, **evolution**.

Science in action

BIG IDEAS IN THIS UNIT

1 Energy is transferred when things happen.
2 Energy is conserved (neither made nor lost) during energy transfers.
3 Light energy from the sun is transferred to plants by photosynthesis.
4 Energy is transferred to living things in a food chain.

4.1 *Forms of energy*

A Energy in action

Energy is transferred when things happen. The cartoons below show six energy transfers.

a Heat energy from wood

b Light energy from a bulb

c Sound energy from vocal cords

d Electrical energy to a computer

e Stored energy to a car

f Movement energy to the wheels

The following two experiments show energy in action.

1 Rub your finger very quickly along the table about 50 times.

2 Collect a battery, a bulb and two wires. Make the bulb light up.

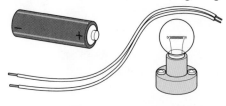

---

1 Describe what you did and what happened in each experiment.
2 How was energy transferred in
  • experiment 1?
  • experiment 2?
3 Copy this table. Use cartoons a–f to help you to complete it.

Energy transferred as	What it can do
a heat energy	keep me warm
b	
c	
d	
e	
f	

B Energy in hiding

1 Write down the title of each of the pictures below and the name of the energy shown.

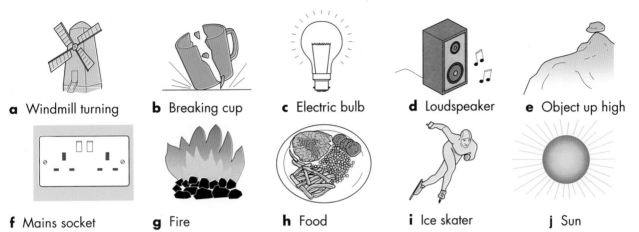

a Windmill turning **b** Breaking cup **c** Electric bulb **d** Loudspeaker **e** Object up high

f Mains socket **g** Fire **h** Food **i** Ice skater **j** Sun

2 Write down the main form of energy that is hidden in each lettered line of the story.

The Visitor

a The winter sky was dark, clear and windless. The full moon cast an eery pale glow upon the shiny

b wet slates of the cottage roofs. An owl hooted and some unknown animal coughed in the shadows. There was nobody about, except Wally. Wally was the village baker.

c He baked all the local bread in a large ancient oven and he started work at 5 a.m. Wally was

d trudging slowly through the slush in the village square because he was carrying a sack of

e coal to work.

He was singing softly to himself . . . 'Happy Christmas to me, Happy Christmas to me, Happy Christmas dear Wally . . .'

Suddenly there was a screech of brakes and a very large vehicle slid to a halt in front of him.

f Its headlamps were full on his face. Wally couldn't see a thing.

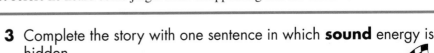

A gruff voice shouted out . . .

'Hey. Is this the village of "Beef-on-Rye?" '

'Yes.'

'. . . and are you Wally Daker, the baker?'

'Yes.'

'Well, Happy Christmas then.'

The person in the vehicle threw down a heavy sack. It hit the ground with a thud just as

g the vehicle zoomed off over Wally's head. Wally opened the sack. Inside was a little yellow

h radio with new batteries, several kilograms of healthy food snacks and a large mail-order catalogue from Greenland.

i Wally switched the radio on, but not before he heard some jingle bells disappearing into the distance.

---

3 Complete the story with one sentence in which **sound** energy is hidden.

4.2 *Energy transfer*

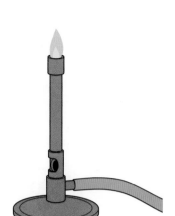

A Energy for a change

Energy can make things happen. Something only happens when energy is transferred.

A Bunsen burner uses gas. The gas has **stored energy**.

The burning gas makes heat. The stored energy of the gas becomes **heat energy**.

Some stored energy also becomes **light energy**.

We can write this as an energy transfer.

Starting energy   *Finishing energy*
Stored   ——————————————▶ Heat and light

Collect a report sheet. Write the energy transfer for each experiment that you finish.

1 Hold the spiral above the heater with the thread.

2 Make the yo-yo go.

3 Press the switch.

4 Wind up the toy and let it go.

5 Pluck the strings.

6 Switch on the disco strobe.

B More energy changes

Copy and complete the table.

Picture	What is happening	Starting energy	Finishing energy
a			
b			
c			

Collect

- Set of energy dominoes

Energy dominoes

Play dominoes in the usual way but match the picture on one domino with the written energy transfer on another.

Copy and complete the sketch of the domino game below. Draw your **own** domino in the middle to link the other two.

stored to heat	[bird]

? what transfer has happened?
draw a suitable diagram

stored to heat	[lamp]

4.3 *Energy accounts*

A The reel wheel

Energy cannot be made from nothing. It also cannot be made into nothing. We say that energy is conserved when it is transferred. All the starting energy must be accounted for after the transfer is complete.

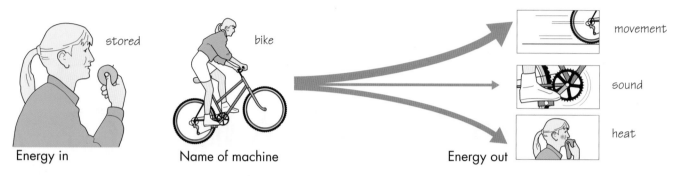

Energy in   stored   bike   Name of machine   Energy out   movement   sound   heat

The energy account would look like this:

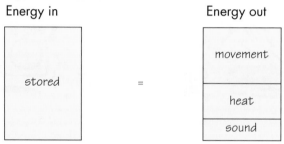

Energy in   Energy out

stored   =   movement / heat / sound

Collect

• Reel wheel kit

The picture below shows a machine called a **reel wheel**. It transfers some of the stored energy in an elastic band into movement energy.

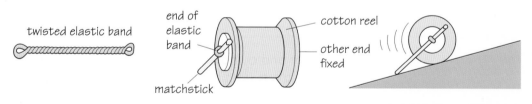

twisted elastic band   end of elastic band   cotton reel   other end fixed   matchstick

Stored energy   Reel wheel   Movement energy

Make a reel wheel. Use the picture above as a guide. Race your reel wheel against a few others in the class.

1 What is a machine? Give two examples.
Write down the energy transfers for each example.

2 Write a full report about making the reel wheel. Include the following:

> ### *Name of machine*
>
> • How the machine works
> • A drawing of the energy account for the machine

B Big machines

Your teacher will show you a big machine; perhaps a steam engine like this.

Discuss

How does the machine work? What are the important energy transfers when the machine is working? What does the energy account look like?

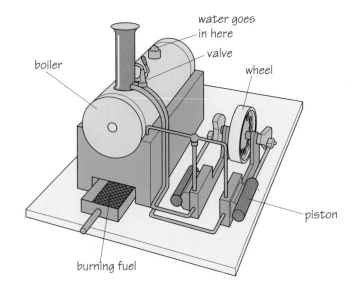

water goes in here

valve

boiler

wheel

piston

burning fuel

a

1 Go to one of the machines set up in the room.
2 Read the instruction card carefully.
3 Make the machine work and study it.

1 Write a report about each of the machines that you study. You should include a description of
   • how the machine works
   • the energy account when it is working.
2 Copy and complete the table for the machines a–d.

Picture	Name of machine	Energy account
a		

b

c

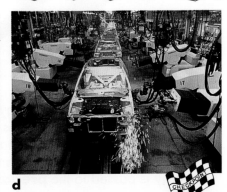

d

CHECKPOINT

4.4 *Energy transfer in living things*

A Food chains

Living things need energy to survive. Energy is transferred through a **food chain**. Look at the three examples.

All food chains have a similar pattern.

1 Light energy from the sun is trapped by green plants.
The light energy is changed into stored energy. This change is called **photosynthesis**.

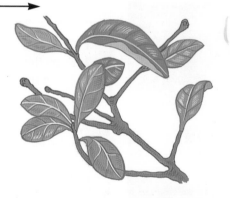

2 The plant uses this energy to grow and stay alive until it is eaten by an animal or it dies.

3 The animal transfers the energy from the plant. Some is stored, some becomes movement, heat and so on. The animal may become the **prey** of another animal. When it is eaten, energy is passed to the **predator**.

Collect

- Food-chain game
- 1 die
- Red and green coloured pencils

Play the food-chain game with a partner. The rules are on the game board.

 1 What is the starting point for all food chains?
2 Which living things carry out photosynthesis?
3 What is the main energy transfer that takes place in photosynthesis?
4 Why is photosynthesis very important?
5 Draw an energy account to show the energy transfers when a predator has eaten its prey.

B A sunny start

You are part of many food chains. You eat food. Energy in food comes from a plant or an animal. This energy can always be traced back to the sun.

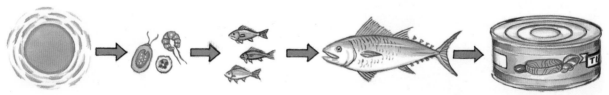

Write down the food chains for three of the foods on the buffet table.

4.5 *Writeabout*

Electricity matters

How was electricity discovered, how is it made, how is it put to work and how is it used sensibly?

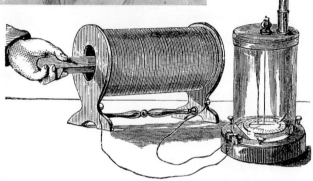

Faraday's work contributed to the discovery of electricity

Making electricity

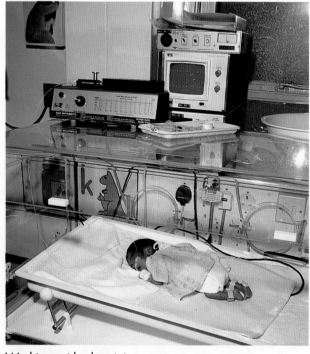

Working with electricity

Using electricity sensibly: the British Standards Institute kitemark is the mark of safety

Project outline

Your writing projects should always be
- in your own words
- about things that are interesting
- neat
- in complete sentences

You can include
- coloured diagrams
- cut-out pictures
- graphs and bar charts
- newspaper clippings

You can find information in
- newspapers
- library books
- science books
- electricity-board leaflets

 Pick **at least two** of the following topics. Your teacher will tell you how much time you have. Write as much as you can about your topics in this time.

Topic	Think about including
1 Discovery of electricity	Important events Important people Important dates
2 Making electricity	Coal, oil and nuclear Hydroelectric Wind and wave Solar and geothermal
3 Working with electricity	In the home In the school In the factory and office
4 Using electricity sensibly	Safety Wasting electricity Saving electricity Future uses

Chinese inventions

We take everyday objects like paper and printed books, umbrellas, matches and paper money for granted. These ideas, and many more, spread to Europe hundreds of years after they had first been discovered in China. China led the world in scientific discovery and invention for 1,500 years. Some of these inventions are described below.

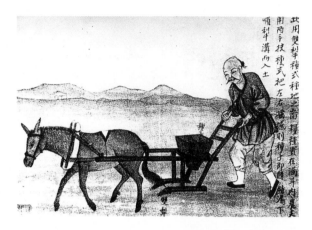

Agriculture: Iron plough
• 6th Century BC in China
• 2,200 years later in Europe

Magnetism: Compass
• 4th Century BC in China
• 1,500 years later in Europe

Industrial technology: Wheelbarrow
• 1st Century BC in China
• 1,300 years later in Europe

Transport: Ship's rudder
• 2nd Century AD in China
• 1,100 years later in Europe

Medicine: Test for diabetes
• 7th Century AD in China
• 1,000 years later in Europe

Engineering: Cast iron
• 4th Century BC in China
• 1,700 years later in Europe

1 Draw a bar chart to show how long it took for the discoveries described above to be used in Europe.
Use the diagram on the left to help you.
2 How do you think the ideas got to Europe from China?
3 Use the books in the classroom or books from a library to find out more about **one** invention from China.
Write a paragraph or make a poster or record a radio report about it. You should include

• a drawing or description of the invention
• why the invention was useful
• how the invention has changed with time.

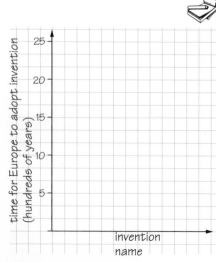

5
Substances

1 Materials are made of substances. We describe substances by using facts.
2 Elements are special substances: they make up all other substances.
3 Metal elements have similar properties; for example, they conduct electricity and heat.
4 Elements join together to form new substances called compounds.
5 In mixtures, the substances are not joined together.

5.1 Describing substances

A Oxygen

We describe substances to people every day. You might describe your teacher's jacket by saying that 'it is wonderful; really modern'. This is your **opinion**. You might describe it as 'cotton, waterproof, with a 30 cm-high figure of Mickey Mouse on the back'. These are **facts** (if they are true!). A really good description of a substance will be full of useful facts.

soft seat

18 gears

loud electronic horn

lunch box

adjustable seat

large tyres

strong frame

lightweight wheels

This bike advert could be improved by giving more facts about the substances in it. For example, the lunch box is made of light, rainproof, green plastic.

Some substances are more difficult to describe. You are going to find out about an **invisible** gas called oxygen. You will describe something that you can only see as bubbles.

Collect

- 2 stoppered tubes of oxygen
- Bunsen burner
- Heatproof mat
- Wooden splints
- Test-tube holder
- Safety glasses

Do experiments **a, b** and **c**.
Use the books available to answer **d** and **e**.

a What is its **appearance**?

b Does it **burn**?
Put a **lighted** splint into the oxygen.
What happens?

c Does it **help things to burn**?
Put a glowing splint into the oxygen.
What happens?

d What is its **melting point**?

e What are its **important uses**?

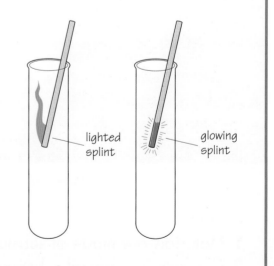

lighted splint

glowing splint

Write a good scientific description of oxygen. Include all the facts that you have found.

B Hydrogen

Hydrogen is another invisible gas. It has many uses.

Rocket fuel

Making margarine

Filling atmospheric research balloons

Making ammonia-based fertilisers

Collect

- 2 stoppered tubes of hydrogen
- Safety glasses
- Anything else you need

Find out about the appearance, burning, melting point and any other uses of hydrogen by experiment and using books.

-POP-

 Write a good scientific description of hydrogen. Include all the facts that you have found.

5.2 *Organising information*

A Introducing metals

A long description is easier to understand if the information is organised in some way. We will put details about substances into three sets

- **appearance**: what the substance looks like
- **properties**: what the substance does
- **uses**: what the substance is used for.

Metal X is common in homes. Perhaps you will recognise it from this description.

Appearance:
Red/brown solid
Shiny and smooth
Sharp edges
Properties:
Melts at 1077°C
Boils at 2567 °C
Good conductor of electricity and heat
Soft metal, can be cut by scissors
1cm^3 weighs 8.9g
Blackens when heated in air
Nothing happens when put in hydrochloric acid
Not magnetic
Uses:
Electrical wiring, jewellery, coins, water pipes, mixed with other metals to make alloys like bronze and brass

Jewellery made from metal X

Collect

- 2 strips of iron
- 2 strips of magnesium
- Battery
- Bulb
- 3 connecting wires
- Magnet

1 Make the following observations, first with iron and then with magnesium. Record your results in note form.

a What is its appearance?

b What is its mass?

c What is its melting point? (You'll need to look this up.)

d Is it a good conductor of heat?

e Is it a good conductor of electricity?

f Is it magnetic?

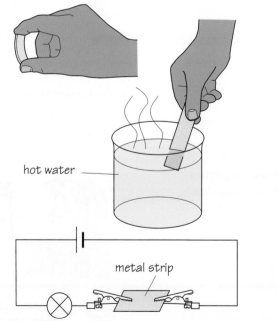

hot water

metal strip

Collect

- Dilute hydrochloric acid
- Test tube
- Bunsen burner and mat
- Tongs
- Safety glasses

2 Use **one** strip of each metal for **each** of the following experiments.

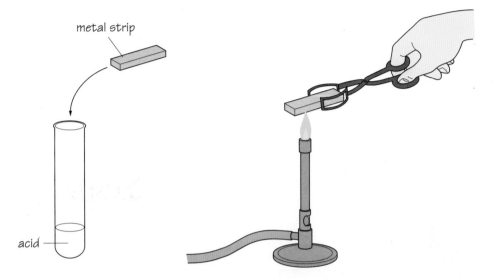

metal strip

acid

a What is the effect of acid on it?

b What is the effect of heat on it? Heat the metal strongly for about a minute. **Do not look directly at the flame.**

1 Read the description of metal X again. Write similar descriptions for iron and for magnesium (use the headings *Appearance* and *Properties*).

2 From your results, write down one possible use for each metal.

B An investigation

Collect

- 2 strips of copper
- 2 strips of zinc
- Safety glasses
- Anything else you need

Find out the properties of the metals zinc and copper.

Write a description for each of these metals.

5.3 *Periodic table*

A The table of elements

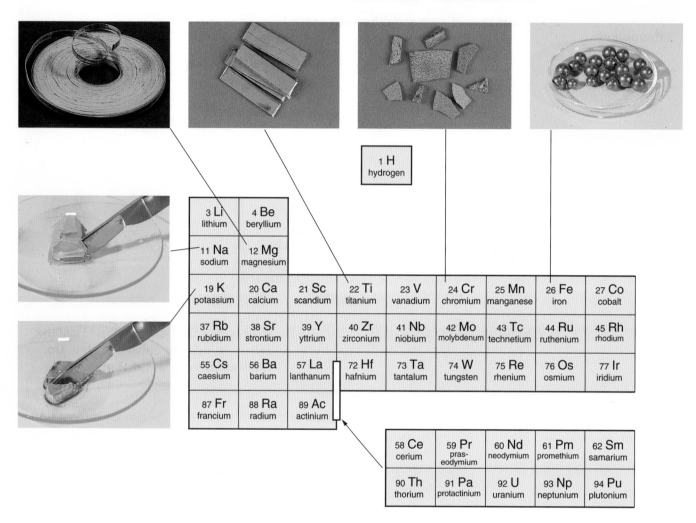

1 H hydrogen								
3 Li lithium	4 Be beryllium							
11 Na sodium	12 Mg magnesium							
19 K potassium	20 Ca calcium	21 Sc scandium	22 Ti titanium	23 V vanadium	24 Cr chromium	25 Mn manganese	26 Fe iron	27 Co cobalt
37 Rb rubidium	38 Sr strontium	39 Y yttrium	40 Zr zirconium	41 Nb niobium	42 Mo molybdenum	43 Tc technetium	44 Ru ruthenium	45 Rh rhodium
55 Cs caesium	56 Ba barium	57 La lanthanum	72 Hf hafnium	73 Ta tantalum	74 W tungsten	75 Re rhenium	76 Os osmium	77 Ir iridium
87 Fr francium	88 Ra radium	89 Ac actinium						

58 Ce cerium	59 Pr pras-eodymium	60 Nd neodymium	61 Pm promethium	62 Sm samarium
90 Th thorium	91 Pa protactinium	92 U uranium	93 Np neptunium	94 Pu plutonium

Scientists describe oxygen, iron and magnesium as elements.
Elements are special: all other substances are made from them.
There are 92 natural elements and some others that have been
made by people. All the elements are listed in a table called the
periodic table.

1 In the periodic table, all the elements have a symbol. Why do
you think these symbols are used?
2 Copy the following list of substances, then underline the elements
in it.
  • water   • oxygen   • silver
  • vinegar   • zinc   • salt
  • bread   • air   • neon
  • sugar   • brass   • carbon

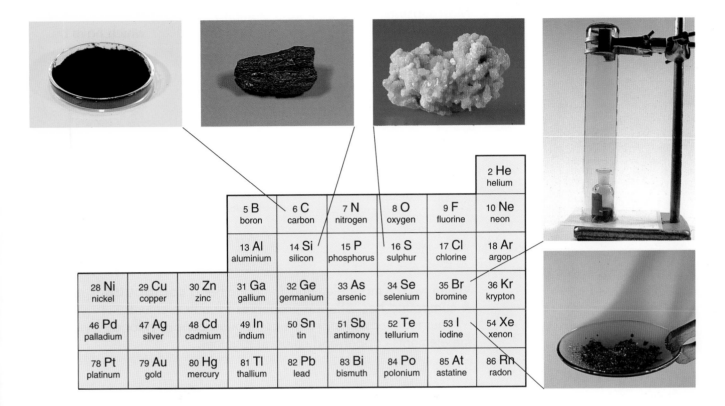

3 List the names and symbols of five elements that you recognise from the periodic table.
   Write down some facts about each one.
4 Where are the metals in the periodic table?

B A chemical code

Use the table to crack this code. Write the message in English.

Scandium + Iodine + (Europium–Uranium) + Nitrogen + Cerium Iodine + Sulphur   Fluorine + Uranium + Nitrogen.

Now try to write your own short coded message.

5.4 Elements make compounds

A Making compounds

Most substances are built from elements which have been joined together. (Just as these words are built from letters which have been joined together.)

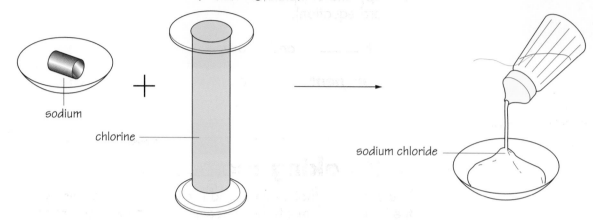

sodium

chlorine

+

sodium chloride

When two or more elements *join* together a **compound** is made. A compound has different properties from its elements.

Your teacher will make the compound copper chloride by joining the elements copper and chlorine together.

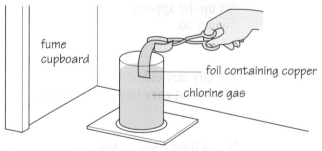

fume cupboard

foil containing copper

chlorine gas

Now you can make a compound yourself.

Collect

- 2 pieces of water-indicator paper
- Dry test tube of hydrogen
- Wooden splint
- Bunsen burner and mat
- Safety glasses

1 Use one piece of water-indicator paper to find out what happens when it is placed in a little water.

2 **Pop** the hydrogen with a lighted splint.

3 Test the tube with water-indicator paper. Look carefully at the edges of the paper.

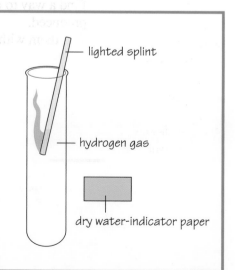

lighted splint

hydrogen gas

dry water-indicator paper

1 What is a compound?

2 Describe your experiment. Include a note of what you did and what happened.

3 Why did you begin with a **dry** test tube containing hydrogen?

4 Copy and complete the following summary (which is called a word equation).

h_____   and   oxygen   join to make   w_____

element   +   e_____   →   c_____

B Breaking compounds

You can show that a compound is made from elements by breaking the join. The elements then become free. The join can sometimes be broken by electricity.

Collect

- Green solid
- 2 carbon rods
- Beaker
- Connecting leads
- Crocodile clips
- Power pack

1 Dissolve a spatula-ful of green solid in about 30cm³ of water.
Set up the apparatus in the diagram.
Switch on.

2 Identify any elements by colour or smell (take great **care** to sniff very gently).

3 If you have time, repeat the experiment with water in place of the green solid.
Find a way to collect the gases which are produced.
Test them with a **lighted** splint.

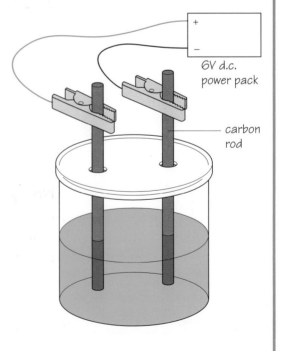

6V d.c. power pack

carbon rod

Collect

- Water
- Bunsen burner and mat
- Wooden splints
- Gas-collecting equipment

1 Describe your experiment(s).
Include a drawing of the apparatus, and a note of what you did and what happened.

2 What do you think the elements in the green solid are?

3 Write a summary (word equation) for your experiment(s)

5.5 *Problem*

Look, no join!

Many materials are mixtures which contain more than one substance. Seawater is an example of a mixture of compounds. Air is an example of a mixture of elements and compounds.

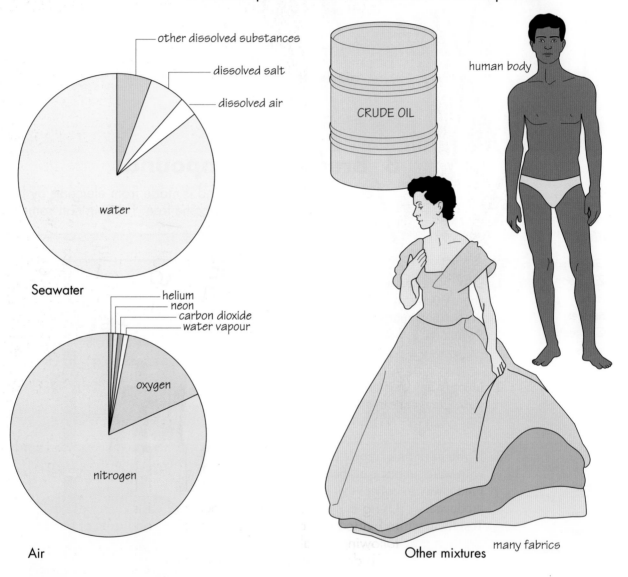

other dissolved substances

dissolved salt

dissolved air

water

Seawater

CRUDE OIL

human body

helium
neon
carbon dioxide
water vapour

oxygen

nitrogen

Air

Other mixtures   many fabrics

Collect

- Some mixture
- Anything else you need
- Safety glasses

Your teacher will mix some substances. Your task is to show that the substances *have not joined* together in the mixture.

Hints
- Watch carefully to see which substances the teacher mixes.
- Look back at Unit 2 for ideas about mixtures.
- Ask for, or look for, facts about the substances in the mixture.

5.6 *Talkabout*

Metals

Metals are very useful.

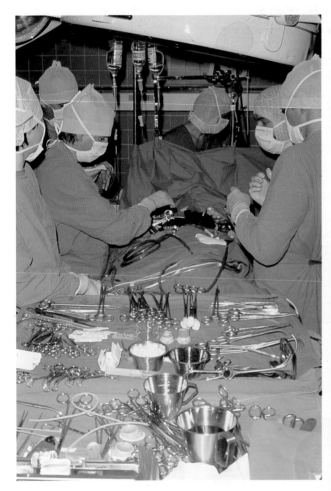

Using the books that your teacher provides, prepare a two-minute talk about the appearance, properties and uses of one of the following metals.

To decide which metal throw a die.

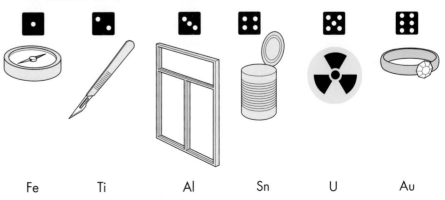

Fe   Ti   Al   Sn   U   Au

5.7 Readabout

Marie Curie

Marie Skolowska was born in 1867 in Poland. Although she came from a poor family, she went to Paris to study science at the University. She was often hungry and cold, but she still managed to become the best student in her class.

She married a French physicist called Pierre Curie when she was 28. Together they worked with a rock called pitchblende. It was interesting because it gave out rays that could go through solid objects. They called these rays **radioactivity**. Marie Curie wanted to find out what was causing this radioactivity.

The Curies' laboratory was just a horrible damp shed. Nevertheless, after eight years, the two scientists managed to separate two new radioactive elements from the pitchblende. They called the two elements polonium (after Poland) and radium.

In 1906 Pierre Curie was knocked down in the road by a horse-drawn carriage and killed. Marie Curie went on to become a professor at the Sorbonne (a university in Paris). She won two Nobel prizes for science and her work became famous throughout the world.

One of the two elements that she discovered, radium, is now used to save many cancer patients. The radiation from radium kills the cancer cells.

1 Copy and complete the personal history file about Marie Curie.

> Name: _____
> Place of birth: _____
> Year of birth: _____
> Three interesting facts:
> _____
> _____
> _____

2 Use the books in the classroom or books from a library to find out more about Marie Curie and her work. Write a paragraph about what you find out. The key words to look up in the index are **Curie**, **radium**, **radiation**.

6

Current thoughts

A Electric charge

The word **charge** is often used in connection with electricity. Here are some examples of charged objects.

You know that electrical charge is there because it can
- move

- make things move.

Collect

- Metal tray
- Plasticine
- Plastic bag

1 Charge on the move

a Press a lump of Plasticine on to a large metal tray.

b Use the Plasticine as a handle and rub the tray over a sheet of plastic.

c Lift the tray and bring it near to your body.

2 Making things move

a Polythene and acetate are insulators. Charge the rods by rubbing with a cloth.

b Balance one on a watch glass so that it can spin freely.

c Bring the other charged rod near it.

d Try all possible combinations. Use freshly charged rods each time.

Collect

- 2 polythene rods
- 2 acetate rods
- 4 watch glasses
- Cloth

The charge on the polythene is called 'negative' and on the acetate 'positive'.

1 Describe the first experiment. Include the energy transfers that take place.
2 Draw a labelled diagram of the second experiment.
3 Copy and complete this table by adding 'attract' or 'repel'.

	Polythene – negative charge	Acetate – positive charge
Polythene – negative charge		
Acetate – positive charge		

B Static

Electric charge can produce electrostatic effects, like movement or a 'shock'.

Do each of these six experiments.

a Paper and comb. Rub the comb on wool. Bring it close to small bits of paper.

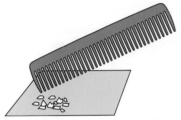

b Rod and water. Use a trickle of water. Rub the rod. Bring it close to the water.

c TV crackle. Turn the TV on. Bring your finger close to the screen.

d Sticky balloon. Rub the balloon on a jersey. Put it on the wall.

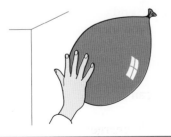

e Warm nylon. Put on a nylon shirt. Blow hot air over it with a hair dryer. Take the shirt off quickly.

f Van de Graaff machine. Your teacher will show you some experiments.

For each experiment

- write a title
- describe what you did
- **explain** how you know that electrical charge was present.

6.2 *Current and voltage*

A Measuring electricity

The amount of charge moving in a circuit is called the **current**. Current is measured in **amperes (A)** using an ammeter.

The battery gives electrical energy to the charge. The **voltage** of the battery indicates how much energy can be given. Voltage is measured in **volts (V)** using a voltmeter.

This ammeter is showing a current of 0.2 A.

This voltmeter is showing a voltage of 1.5 V.

Collect

- Ammeter
- Voltmeter
- Bulb
- 9 wires
- 4 batteries
- Graph paper

1 Set up this circuit.

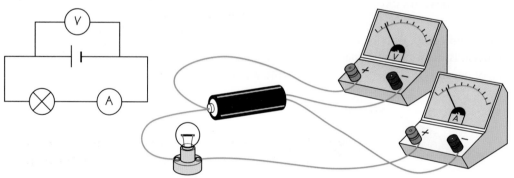

Note • Connect the **black** terminal of the ammeter to the **negative** (−) end of the battery and the other terminal to the bulb.
  • Connect the **black** terminal of the voltmeter to the **negative** (−) end of the battery and the other voltmeter terminal to the positive end.

2 Find out what happens to the voltage and the current when you increase the number of batteries in the circuit.

1 What is the difference between current and voltage?
2 Make a table to record the number of batteries, voltage and current.
3 Draw a line graph of current against voltage.
4 Describe what the graph shows.

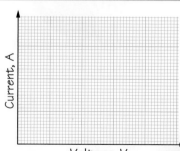

B Different components

Collect

- Another bulb
- Buzzer

1 Set up this circuit again.

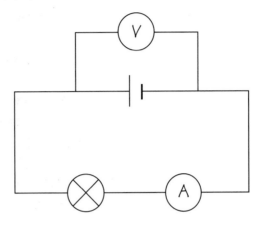

2 Find out what happens to the voltage and the current when you
  a   add another bulb
  b   replace the bulb with a buzzer
  c   replace the bulb with a different type of bulb.

 Copy the following passage about your experiments. Put the words on the left in the correct place in the passage. (A word can be used more than once.)

voltage   circuit   charge

increases   decreases

stays the same

Current is the amount of _____ which moves in a _____. In a circuit the current _____ as the number of bulbs increases. The current _____ as the number of batteries increases. The battery gives the charge electrical energy. A battery with a higher _____ gives more electrical energy. The voltage _____ as the number of bulbs increases. The voltage _____ as the number of batteries increases.

6.3 Rows and branches

A House lighting

There are two important ways of connecting bulbs in a circuit:

- in **series**

The bulbs are all in
a single row

- in **parallel**

The bulbs are
in branches

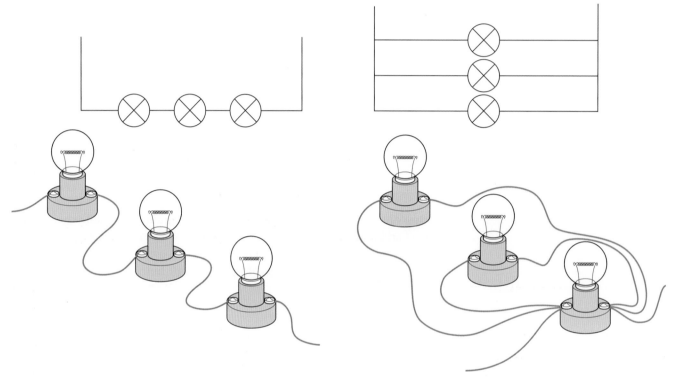

One of these ways of connecting bulbs is used to solve important design problems in your home. In your home you want:

- **bright** lights
- lights that **stay on** even when one bulb breaks or is removed.

Collect

- Parts needed to build circuits
- Resource sheet
- Ammeter

1 Build a series circuit and a parallel circuit, using two batteries in each. Find out which circuit would be better for house lights.
2 Collect a resource sheet. Discuss with a partner what you think the current will be at the points marked on the sheet. Now use an ammeter to check your predictions. Write your actual **measurements** on the sheet and stick it in your book.

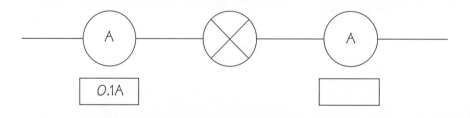

0.1A

1 Write about your experiments.
Include:

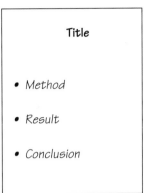

Title

• *Method*

• *Result*

• *Conclusion*

2 Use your measurements of current to **explain** why one circuit is better than the other for house lighting.

B Missing words

Copy the circuit diagrams below. Complete them by writing in the missing ammeter readings. Note: all the buzzers are identical.

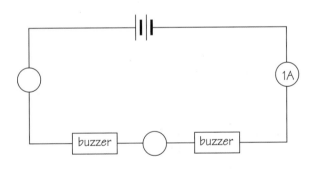

Series

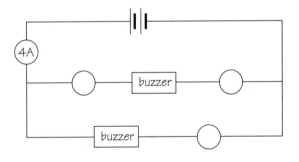

Parallel

Copy and complete the passage about these circuits. Words in the list can be used more than once.

electrical   equal   split
used up   the same   sound

In the series circuit the current is _____ at all points. The current carries _____ energy to the buzzers where it is transferred into _____ energy. The current is not _____.
   In a parallel circuit the current is _____ into each branch. If the components on each branch are the same the current on each branch will be _____. The current is not _____.

6.4 Switch gaps

A A switch in time

Electric charge moves through some materials (such as copper) more easily than others (such as water). Water has a higher electrical **resistance** than copper. When resistance is high, the current is low. The idea of resistance helps us to

- make a simple switch to turn the current on and off
- make a dimmer switch to raise and lower the current.

Collect

- Switches
- Metal foil *or* ring pull tops
- Bulb
- 2 batteries
- 4 connecting wires
- 2 crocodile clips

Collect

- Parts needed to build the circuit
- Copper wire
- Nichrome wire
- Ammeter

1 Look at a display switch. Find out what happens inside the switch when it operates. Design and build a circuit with a simple switch in it.

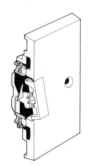

Symbol for a switch

2 A dimmer switch makes a bulb dimmer by increasing the resistance to the current. Build the circuit below.

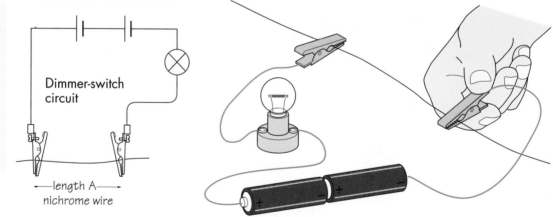

Dimmer-switch circuit

length A nichrome wire

a Find out what happens to resistance when you change the length of the wire (length A).
b Find out what happens to resistance when you replace the nichrome wire with copper wire. (Design a fair test.)

 Write a report about your investigation of resistance using the dimmer-switch circuit. Include title, method, results and conclusion.

B Continuity tester

An electric current cannot usually flow across a gap in a circuit. The resistance in the gap is very high. For example, these gaps stop the current.

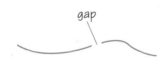

Broken wire

Broken fuse

Broken bulb

An electrician uses a **continuity tester** to find a gap in a broken circuit. The damage is repaired by closing the gap.

A multimeter can be used as a continuity tester.

This is also a continuity tester.

It contains this circuit.

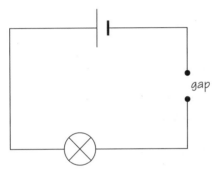

1 **Collect** a set of test wires. Build and use the circuit shown above to find out which wires are broken.
2 **Collect** a multimeter and a set of electrical components. Your teacher will show you how to use the multimeter. Use the multimeter to check
   a the broken wires from your first experiment
   b the electrical components for gaps.

1 Describe how you used a continuity tester to find a broken wire.
2 The multimeter was set to measure resistance.
   a What is the meaning of low **resistance**?
   b Does an air gap have a high or a low resistance to current?

6.5 *Plugs*

A Wire a plug

1 Examine the test plug and the flex. Find the important parts.

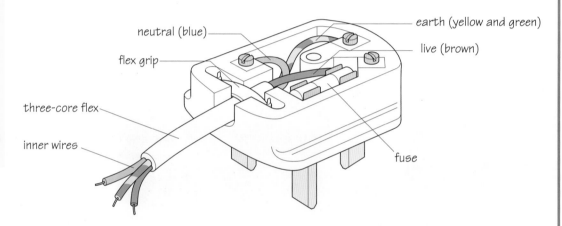

neutral (blue)
flex grip
three-core flex
inner wires
earth (yellow and green)
live (brown)
fuse

2 Strip about 5 cm of the outer cover of the flex. Do not cut through the cover of the inner wires.
3 Put the flex under the cord grip. Tighten the screws of the cord grip.
4 Cut about 2 cm off the brown covered and the blue covered wires.
5 Strip about 0.5 cm of the plastic cover from the three wires.
6 Put the bare wires into the correct terminals like those in the picture.
   Remember: BRown goes to **B**ottom **R**ight
   BLue goes to **B**ottom **L**eft
   Third green/yellow wire goes to **T**op.
7 Tighten the terminal screws.
8 Check your wiring with your teacher.

 1 Copy and complete the table.

	Name of terminal		
	Neutral	Live	Earth
Where it is			
Colour of wire			

2 What is the cord grip for?
3 Why is the main part of the plug made of plastic?
4 What should be done to correct each of these faulty situations?

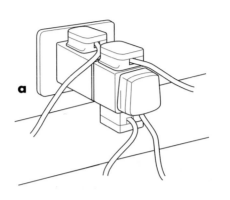
a

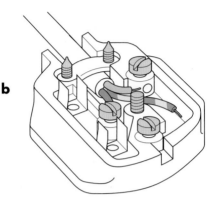
b

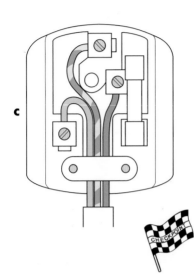
c

B Safe practice

Many accidents in the home are caused by electrical faults. You should know how to use electricity safely. You should also know how to correct a fault safely.

Decide whether you would be satisfied with these changes. Explain your answer.

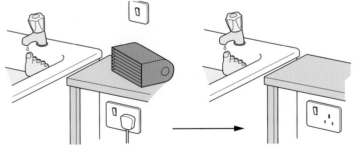

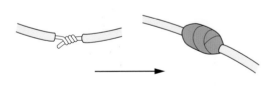

a Before   After

b Before   After

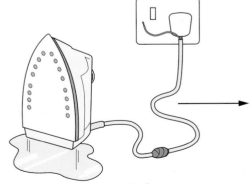

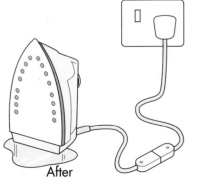

c Before   After

6.6 *Problem*

Beat the burglar

Many people worry about burglars. They ask 'What can we do to keep the burglars out of our home?' You might ask 'What can we do to keep burglars out of our classroom?'

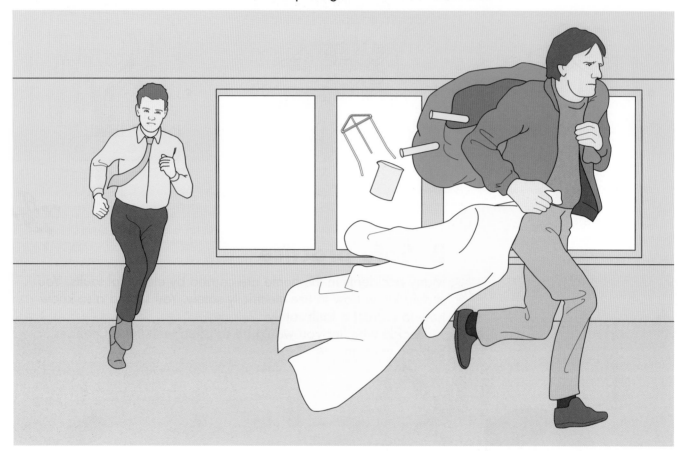

You can make your classroom burglar-proof by designing, making and fitting different types of burglar alarm.

Collect

- Electrical components
- Hint sheet (if needed)

- Work in a group.
- Discuss
  - how a burglar could get into the classroom
  - where burglar alarms could be fitted
  - how a switch could set off a buzzer or light a bulb.
- Design several different switches and try them out.
- Build and fit your switches. Check that they work effectively. Make alterations if they don't.

Produce a group poster of your designs. Label the designs to show how the switches work. All the designs can be compared by making a class display.

6.7 *Talkabout*

A world without electricity

Imagine a world without electricity. Take away the electricity from each picture below.

- What would the problems be?
- How would you solve them?

Electricity for leisure

Electricity for lighting

Electricity for communication

Electricity for transport

Lewis Latimer

Today we can buy light bulbs that last a long time; for example, low energy light bulbs. The first working light bulb was invented by Thomas Edison but it wasn't very effective. The filament – where electrical energy is transferred to light energy – burned out too quickly.

The American Lewis Latimer made a breakthrough by inventing a long-lasting filament. He registered his invention in 1881 and was asked to join a group of inventors called Edison's Pioneers. He wrote the first book on electric lighting and went on to set up street lighting systems in New York and Montreal.

Lewis Latimer's early life was very difficult. He was born in 1848 and his parents were runaway slaves. He fought for the Union Navy in the American Civil War.

After the war he worked as an office boy. He taught himself to be a fine draughtsman during this time. Latimer then became friends with Alexander Graham Bell and made the patent drawings for Bell's invention – the telephone. He was a very able and determined man – full of ideas and eager to learn. In 1879 he met another inventor, Herman Maxim, who was in charge of an electric lighting company. Latimer learned everything he could about electricity and two years later invented his light bulb with a long-lasting filament.

Latimer died in 1928 when he was eighty years old.

 1 Copy and complete the personal history file about Lewis Latimer.

> Name: _____
> Place of birth: _____
> Year of birth: _____
> Three interesting facts:
> _____
> _____
> _____

2 Use books in the classroom or from a library to find out more about Lewis Latimer and the development of the light bulb. The key words to look up are **Latimer**, **Edison**, **Maxim**, **light bulb**, **filament**.

7
Small beginnings

BIG IDEAS IN THIS UNIT

1 All living things are made up of cells.
2 Each part of a cell has a job to do.
3 There are many different types of cell. The structure of a cell helps it to carry out its job.
4 Reproduction in animals and plants follows a similar pattern.

7.1 *Look small*

A Microscope parts

Your eyes need help to see very small things. A microscope magnifies small things, making them appear bigger. There are different kinds of microscopes.

Light microscope

Tick, × 10

Scanning electron microscope

Tick, × 30

You are going to use a light microscope like this.

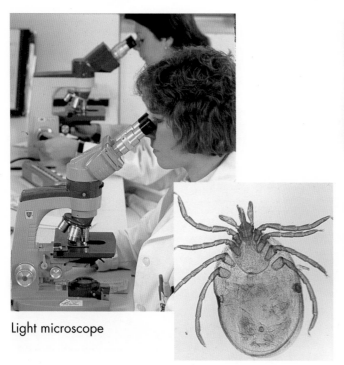

eyepiece lens (magnifies)

focus control (gives you a sharp picture)

objective lens (magnifies)

stage (holds the slide)

mirror (shines light through what you want to see)

A light microscope will magnify things. Light is shone through the object so that you can see it. The object must therefore be very thin.

1 **Collect** a diagram of the light microscope and stick it into your book. Complete the diagram by adding labels. Read and learn the rules on the diagram.
2 Make a table of two columns in your book to show the **parts** of the microscope and what each part **does**.

1 **Collect** slide A. Focus the microscope on the
   slide. Watch the letter when you move the slide
   up/down and left/right.
   a What is the letter on slide A?
   b Describe how the letter moves.

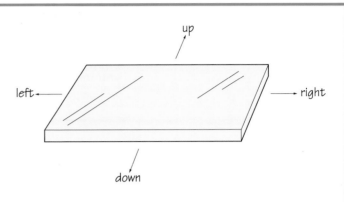

2 **Collect** slide B. There is a word on slide B. It
   has five letters. The first letter is on the second
   slide down; find this. The next letter is on the
   last slide; find this. Focus up, then down, then
   up again to read the next three letters.

   What is the word on the slide?

B Using a microscope

1 **Collect** a fibre slide. Use the microscope and the
   drawings below to identify your fibre.

   Draw your fibre. Name it.

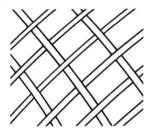

Nylon   Cotton

2 **Collect** a clean slide. Use it to look at some
   interesting things with your microscope. For
   example, cloth, hair, paper, fluff, leaves . . .

   Make a large drawing of everything that you
   look at.

7.2 Building bricks

A Cells

About 300 years ago Robert Hooke made an important discovery using a microscope. You are going to see what he discovered. First you must know how to prepare a microscope slide. Your teacher will show you how.

1 Make a slide of a thin piece of onion skin.

   Describe how you prepared the slide.

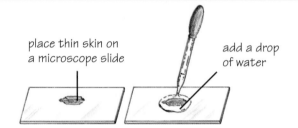

place thin skin on a microscope slide

add a drop of water

lower a cover slip onto the onion skin

it should look like this

2 Look at the slide with the microscope. Use low magnification.

   Look for a pattern on the slide.
   What does the pattern look like?

3 Add one drop of iodine stain to the slide. Replace the cover slip. Look at the slide again. Use a higher magnification.

   Iodine helps to show more clearly that plants are made of tiny units called **cells**. Draw two of the cells. Show as much detail as you can.

Some very small plants and animals have only one cell, but most plants and animals are made up of many cells. Cells are very small. In one cubic millimetre of human blood there are more than five million cells!

A living cell has different parts which do different jobs.

Most cells have

1 membrane which controls the movement of substances in and out of the cell

2 cytoplasm where chemical changes take place

3 nucleus which controls the cell

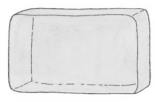  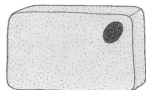

Most plant cells also have

4 cell wall which gives the cell shape and support

5 chloroplasts which make food using sunlight

6 vacuole which holds a watery solution

 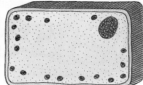 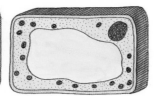

1 **Collect** a cells diagram and stick it into your book. Label all the important parts of the animal cell and the plant cell.
2 Copy and complete the table below.

Part of the cell	What the part does
1	
2	

B More cells

> 1 Make a slide of the green plant material.
> 2 Look at the slide using the microscope.

Draw two of the plant cells. Label six important parts of the cells in your drawing.

7.3 *Special cells*

A Cell types

Most living things are made up of different types of cells. The cells look different because they are built to do different jobs.

Sex cell

A sex cell carries information. A male makes sex cells called sperm. A female makes sex cells called eggs.

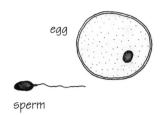

egg

sperm

Muscle cell

A muscle cell can make itself shorter to produce movement.

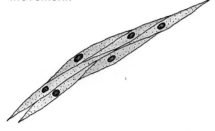

Brain nerve cell

A brain nerve cell passes information on through its connections.

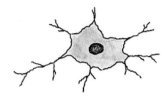

Motor nerve cell

A motor nerve cell controls movement. It passes a message from the brain to a muscle.

White blood cell

A white blood cell fights disease.

Skin cell

A skin cell forms part of a layer which protects the body.

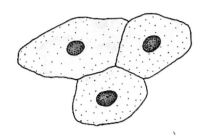

Collect

- Microscope slide
- Seedling root
- Slide of plant leaf

1 Make a slide of the seedling root. It has been put in a stain solution to make the cells easier to see.

2 Look at the root under the microscope. Look for the root hair cells. Compare them to the other root cells.

3 Draw one root hair cell to show its structure (what it looks like).

4 Look at the prepared slide of a plant leaf. There are four or five layers. Compare the different cell types.

5 Draw a cell from each layer. Label each cell by writing down what job it might be built for.

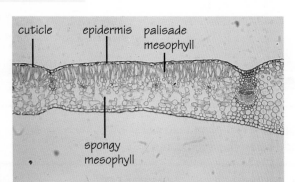

cuticle   epidermis   palisade mesophyll

spongy mesophyll

Section through the leaf of a Christmas rose plant

1 How does the structure of a root cell help it to take in water from the soil?

2 Name six different types of human body cell.

3 Choose two types of human body cell. Use the information available to find out more about your chosen cells.

   a List three important facts about each of your chosen cells.

   b Draw the cells. Label them to show how their structure helps them to carry out their job.

4 Look at the photograph of human sex cells.

Human egg with sperms (× 400 approximately)
Only one egg is usually released at a time. Many millions of sperm are released at a time.

Copy and complete the following table.

	Human sperm	Human egg
Shape (draw)		
Size		
Number		

B More cells

Collect

- Microscope slide
- Cover slip
- Slice of plant stem
- Bottle of stain

1 Make a slide of the plant stem. Add a drop of stain.

2 Look at the stem under the microscope using low magnification.

3 Find three different types of cell.

How an expert cuts a slice from a plant stem

look here
(cells for protection)

look here
(cells for carrying water)

look here
(cells for support)

4 Draw the shape of each cell in your book. Write down the job that each cell does. Give your drawing a title.

7.4 *Making new life*

A Animal reproduction

Every living thing must reproduce, either sexually or asexually. In most animals sexual reproduction takes place. The diagram shows the important events in stickleback reproduction. Vertebrates all have the same pattern of events. The details of what happens during each event may be different.

Important event	What happens
Maturity Female swollen with eggs Male with red breast	The male animal makes sperm. The female animal makes eggs. The animal is only now able to reproduce. It is an adult.
Courtship and mating Female lays eggs in a nest Male follows the female and spreads sperm over the eggs	The male and the female meet. This is courtship. The male sperm is put near the female egg cell. This is mating.
Fertilisation Magnified many times	The sperm enters the egg cell. This happens outside the female body in most fish and amphibians. It happens inside the body in reptiles, birds and mammals.
Embryo growth 	The fertilised egg divides and grows to form an embryo. The embryo contains thousands of cells.
Birth 	The baby animal is born. In many animals it hatches from an egg. In mammals it comes directly from the mother's body.
Growth 	The baby animal gets bigger. It grows into a mature adult.

1 **Collect** a summary of this diagram and complete it. Stick it into your book.

2 Copy the following passage. Put the words on the left in the correct place in the passage.

egg   sexual   asexual

dogs   frogs   born

grows   outside

inside   reproduce

adult

There are two kinds of reproduction, sexual and _____ reproduction. Fertilisation occurs during _____ reproduction when the sperm meets the _____. In some animals such as humans and _____ fertilisation happens _____ the body of the female. In other animals such as _____ and fish, fertilisation happens _____ the body of the female. The fertilised egg _____ into a baby animal and is _____. The baby grows to maturity and becomes an _____. The animal is now ready to _____.

B Life cycles

Look at the pictures below. They show some important events in the life cycle of a turtle, but the order of events is mixed up.

Write down the correct order of events.

a

b

c

d

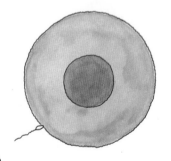

e

f

Collect

• Die
• Timer
• Life Cycles
  information
  sheet

Now play the game Life Cycles. This game involves sorting out the life cycles of a fish, a frog and a chicken. The information sheet explains how to play the game.

7.5 *People*

A Human reproduction

The table summarises some important events in the life of a person. All these events are linked to sexual reproduction.

Important event	*What happens*
Maturity	The woman produces female sex cells called eggs or ova. The man makes male sex cells called sperm. Only now is the person able to reproduce. She or he has reached sexual maturity.
Courtship and mating	The woman and the man meet and get to know each other. If they mate then sperm are passed into the body of the woman.
Fertilisation ovum / sperm	The sperm swim towards the ovum. One sperm enters the ovum to fertilise it.
Embryo growth 6 weeks / 8 weeks	The fertilised ovum divides again and again to form a ball of cells. This embryo keeps on growing and develops into a baby.
Birth	The baby is born. In humans the baby comes from the mother's body. The baby begins to breathe and to take food.
Growth baby / child / adult	The baby gets bigger and grows into a mature adult.

sperm   inside
embryo   reproduce
ovum   mating
fertilisation   adult

1 Collect a summary of this table and complete it. Stick it into your book.

2 Copy the following passage. Put the words on the left in the correct place in the passage.

Human fertilisation occurs _____ the woman's body. During _____ the sperm are squirted into the woman. They swim to meet the _____. One _____ enters it and forms an embryo. This is called _____. The _____ then grows in the woman's body. After about nine months a baby is born. It eventually reaches maturity and becomes an _____. The person is now able to _____.

B The human life cycle

You can learn more about the important events in human reproduction by using the resources in the classroom such as worksheets, books and videos. At the end of this work **choose one** of the following ways of recording what you have learned.

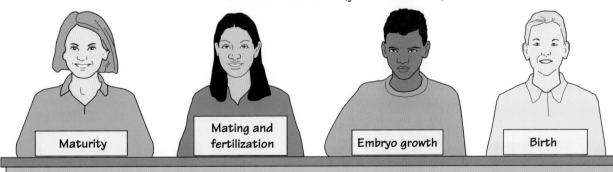

1 With your group

a Watch a short section of video about reproduction *with the sound off*. Write and perform a sound track.

b As a panel of experts research *all* the events. Answer questions from an invited audience (your classmates).

Maturity · Mating and fertilization · Embryo growth · Birth

2 By yourself

a Design and draw a poster to explain one of the events.

b Prepare and give (or record) a talk about one of the events.

7.6 *Flowers*

A Plant reproduction

The diagram shows some important events in the sexual life of a flowering plant. All these events are part of reproduction.

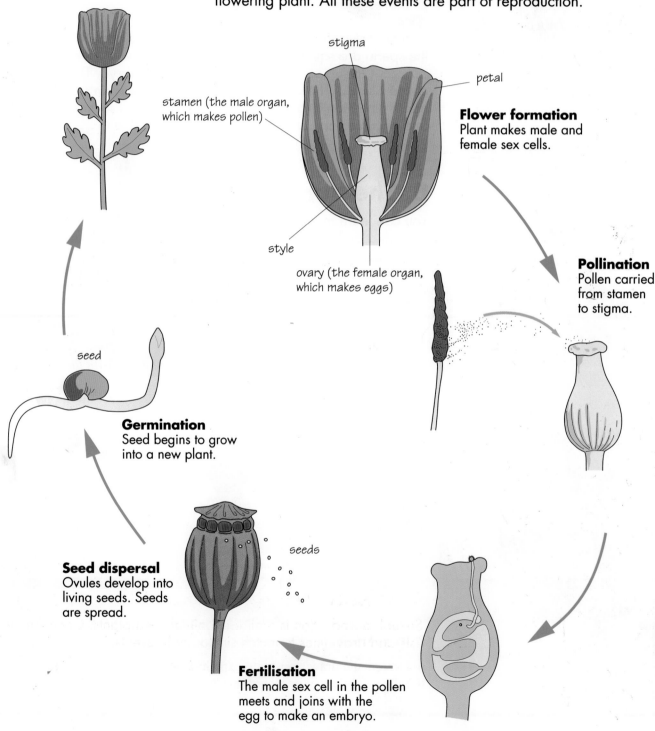

stigma

petal

stamen (the male organ, which makes pollen)

Flower formation
Plant makes male and female sex cells.

style

ovary (the female organ, which makes eggs)

Pollination
Pollen carried from stamen to stigma.

seed

Germination
Seed begins to grow into a new plant.

seeds

Seed dispersal
Ovules develop into living seeds. Seeds are spread.

Fertilisation
The male sex cell in the pollen meets and joins with the egg to make an embryo.

Collect a summary of this diagram and complete it. Stick it into your book.

1 Gently pull the flower apart using the tweezers.

2 Find
  • a petal
  • a stamen (the male part)
  • the stigma, style and ovary (the female parts)
  • ovules

3 Stick these parts of the flower into your book and label them.

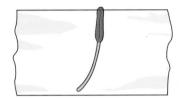

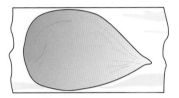

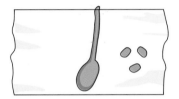

1 Write a sentence to describe what pollination is.
2 During pollination the pollen gets stuck to the stigma. The drawings below show what happens next.

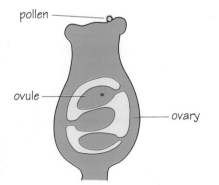

pollen

ovule

ovary

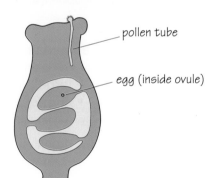

pollen tube

egg (inside ovule)

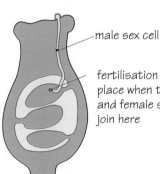

male sex cell

fertilisation takes place when the male and female sex cells join here

Describe how the male sex cell fertilises the egg. Use the words in the drawings.

B Main events

Sexual reproduction is similar in animals and plants. Copy the two lists and draw lines to match similar main events.

Plant	*Animal*
Fertilisation	Birth
Flower formation	Courtship and mating
Germination	Embryo growth
New plant	Fertilisation
Pollination	Growth
Seed dispersal	Maturity

7.7 Problem

Site the seed

Your problem is to advise a government about the best place to plant a new food crop.
Here is a sketch map of the country.

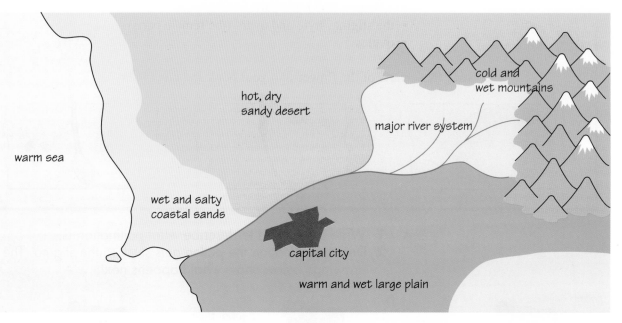

You know that seed germinates in a few days. You have to find out how well the plant will germinate and grow in the
- sandy desert
- large plain
- mountains
- coastal sands.

Collect

- Packet of seeds
- Anything else you need

Design some experiments to solve the problem.

Hints
- The seed will germinate on wet paper.

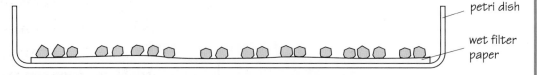

- You will have to make sure that any test you do is **fair**.
- You will have to think about measurements/observations.

Now solve the problem.

 Write a short report for the government. Include a description of your experiment(s) and a bar graph of your results. Give advice about the best place to plant the crop.

7.8 *Talkabout*

Letters page

These letters are about imaginary science problems. Discuss the letters with your partner. Decide how to answer each letter (kindly).

Dear Auntie Katie
   I can't seem to get pollinated. My friends all say I'm not bad looking but no insect will come near me. Can you give me any advice. I enclose a recent photo
      Yours,
      Paula N.

Dear Auntie Katie
All the men on T.V. have hairy chests. I don't even have any under my arms. Am I normal I am 9 years old
Fluff

Dear Katie
   Why is it that salmon like myself have to make so many eggs? Chickens only make a few; humans make even less. No wonder they have time to go fishing! Please explain why life is so unfair to fish
      your friend,
      Small Fry

Dear Auntie Katie
This is my photo. You can see that I am not smiling. I live in a pond that is full of wonderful, beautiful frogs. They all have so much fun and they mate every spring. I am missing out. What is wrong with me? Tod Pole

Australopithecus africanus

The human race

The story of the human race began 5 million years ago in East Africa. Scientists study fossil remains to piece together the human story. Unfortunately the fossil record is not complete so there is not enough evidence to be certain about the details. However, scientists believe that humans developed or evolved from ape-like creatures.

In 1924 the 5 million-year-old fossil skull of a baby was found in South East Africa. It was different from an ape skull in two important ways. The position of the hole for the spinal cord showed that this creature stood upright. The teeth were small and square. They were not designed for catching animal food or for rooting about on the ground. So this animal must have used its hands to feed. Scientists called it *Australopithecus africanus*.

For several million years there was no great change. Then 1 million years ago *Homo erectus* appeared. It seems that this early human spread far out of Africa into Northern Europe and China where there is evidence that these people used fire and made tools. They had a much bigger brain than *Australopithecus*, a flatter face, and a very upright stance.

About 200,000 years ago Neanderthal man appears in the fossil record. The brain is now the same size as in modern humans. Neanderthal man survived an ice age in Europe by being inventive and producing a wider range of finer tools.

The earliest people we would recognise as modern humans appear about 35,000 years ago. We call them *Homo sapiens*— wise people. Scientists can't agree who they were descended from — perhaps Neanderthals or perhaps a new line of *Homo erectus* spreading out of Africa for a second time. Apart from their fossil remains, these early people left evidence, in tools and art, of how they lived.

1 Draw a time line starting 5 million years ago and show 4 possible ancestors of the human race.
2 Use the books in the classroom or books from a library to find out more about one of the human ancestors. Use the information to make a poster for a class display. Keywords to look up in the index are **Australopithecus**, **Homo erectus**, **Peking man**, **Neanderthal man**, **caveman**, **Stone Age**.

Extensions

Turning yellow

During a science experiment you look for some kind of change. It is a good idea to check your observations by doing the experiment again.

Collect

- A marked test tube
- Test-tube rack
- Safety glasses
- Clear liquid
- Dark green liquid
- Bottle of acid
- Dropper

a Pour clear liquid into the test tube up to the marked line.

b Add two drops of dark green liquid.

c Find out how many drops of acid are needed to change the colour to yellow.

d Repeat the experiment (steps a–c) to check your observation.

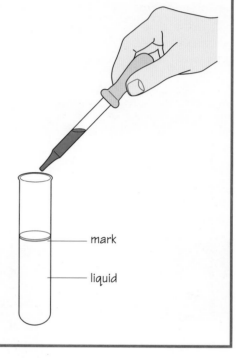

mark

liquid

1 What happened when the dark green liquid and the clear liquid were mixed?

2 Copy and complete the diagram to show all the colours that you observed.

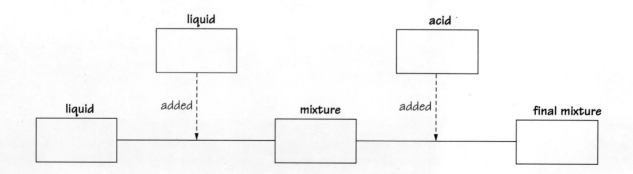

liquid

acid

liquid   added   mixture   added   final mixture

3 How many drops of acid did you need to add
  a the first time?
  b the second time?
4 Why was the experiment repeated?

Salt, vinegar and (marble) chips

Collect

Find out what happens when you add vinegar to salt and when you add vinegar to marble chips.

Collect

- Bottle of salt
- Bottle of marble chips
- Bottle of vinegar
- Test-tube rack
- 2 test tubes
- Safety glasses

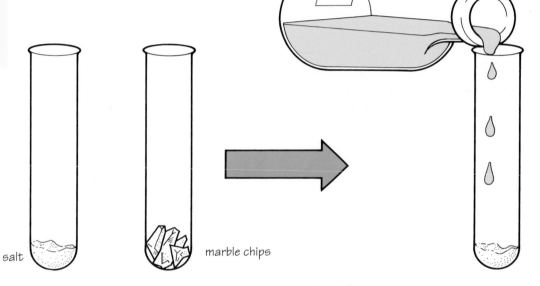

salt   marble chips

You only need to use a small amount to see a good result.

 Write a short report about your experiment. You should include

<u>Your own title</u>

The method (what you did):

The result (what happened):

More measurement puzzles

Solve the following puzzles. For each puzzle you should copy the title and
- write a sentence to explain how you solved each puzzle
- record each measurement.

How do you measure . . . ?

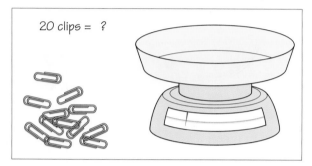

20 clips = ?

a the mass of one paper clip

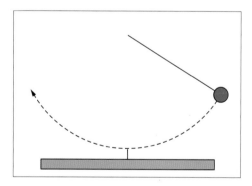

mass A + mass B

b the mass of 50cm³ of water

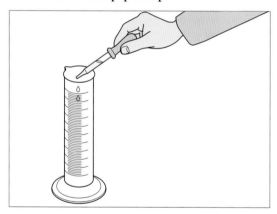

c the volume of one drop of water

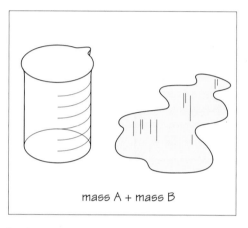

d the time of one swing

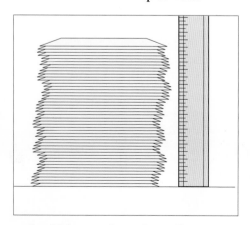

e the thickness of one sheet of paper

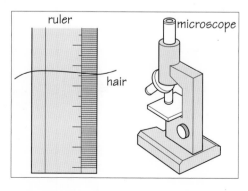

ruler   microscope

hair

f the thickness of one hair

Baby Catriona's milk

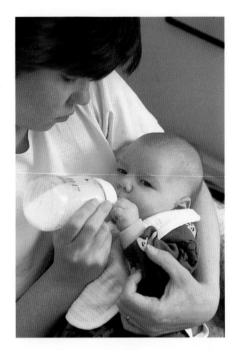

Baby Catriona is less than one year old. She has the same birthday as **you**. Use today's date to work out how old she is.

The milk in her bottle is made from powder. She is very young so the milk has to be exactly right. It must not contain too much powder (which would make her sick) or too little (which would make her weak). The table shows how much milk powder to use to make a bottle for Catriona.

FEEDING GUIDE

To make each 1 fl oz (28ml) of baby milk add 1 level scoop of granules to 1 fl oz (28ml) of hot (60°C) previously boiled water. **Always use the scoop provided to measure the granules. Do not add extra granules.**

Feeding guide Age up to	Average Weight		No. of feeds per 24 hours	Level scoops of milk powder per feed	Quantity of water per feed	
	lb	kg			floz	ml
2 weeks	7³/₄	3.5	6	3	3	85
1 month	8¹/₂	3.9	5	4	4	115
2 months	10¹/₂	4.7	5	5	5	140
3 months	12	5.4	5	6	6	170
4 months	13³/₄	6.2	5	6	6	170
5 months	15¹/₄	6.9	5	7	7	200
6 months	16³/₄	7.6	5	7	7	200

From 6 months onwards: the latest recommendations state that it is beneficial to continue to use an infant milk as a drink or cup feed up to 12 months of age instead of cow's milk. For 7 to 12 months follow the feeding guide for 6 months.

Collect

- Milk bottle
- Powdered milk
- Scoop
- Small knife

1 You already know Catriona's age. From the table above work out how many scoops of powder to use for her bottle.

2 Take *warm* water from a kettle or tap and make up Catriona's bottle. (A baby's milk bottle is usually made up with boiled water.)

Write a note to Catriona's mother explaining how you made her bottle of milk. Make sure that her mother knows how much powder you used and why you chose that amount.

Cool it

In an experiment a scientist often collects evidence about **change**. For example, the colour of a liquid may change, the mass of a solid may change, or the temperature may change.

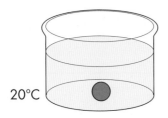

20°C

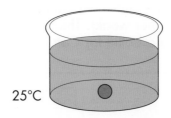

25°C

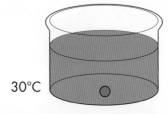

30°C

Often the evidence can be shown in a line graph.

Collect

- Thermometer
- Elastic band
- Sheet of graph paper
- Piece of cottonwool
- Bottle of propanone
- Clock or watch or timer

1 Wrap the cotton wool carefully around the bulb of the thermometer. Hold it in place with the elastic band.

make sure you can see the start of the scale

2 Copy the table below into your book.

	Time					
	Start	2 min	4 min	6 min	8 min	10 min
Temperature						

3 Read and record the start temperature. Add ten drops of propanone to the cotton wool and start the clock. The propanone will evaporate and cool the cotton wool. Look at the clock:

4 Record the temperature every two minutes until the table is complete.

 Draw a line graph of your results. (The hints below may help you.) **Explain** what your graph means.

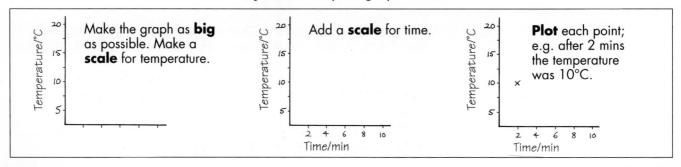

Make the graph as **big** as possible. Make a **scale** for temperature.

Add a **scale** for time.

Plot each point; e.g. after 2 mins the temperature was 10°C.

Fairly dry

All these products contain a liquid. The liquid must have these properties: it must be *safe* *and* it must dry up quickly.

Baby wipes

Antiseptic wipes

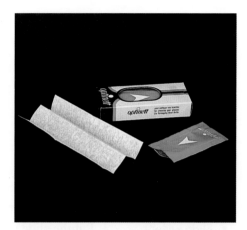
Lens wipes

Some liquids evaporate more easily than others. Investigate how quickly three different liquids dry up.

Collect

- 3 pieces of tissue
- 3 droppers
- Bottle of alcohol
- Water
- Bottle of propanone
- Timer
- Scissors

Hints
1 **Do not** use any flames or any other source of direct heat.
2 Make sure that your experiment is fair.
   (The cartoon shows an unfair experiment.)

3 Use a timer.

1 Write a report about this experiment. Include the method (a description of what you did), a drawing and a note of your results.
2 What did you do to make your experiments fair?
3 What other properties must a good wipe have?

Vanishing varnish

Water is not the only solvent. Other liquids can also dissolve substances. Many cleaning fluids contain other solvents, so do glues.

CARE
Many solvents are **harmful**. Some solvents are **flammable**.

Harmful

Flammable

Collect

- Slide with 5 streaks of nail varnish
- Cotton wool
- Tweezers
- 5 solvents (water, propanone, alcohol, turpentine, ethyl ethanoate)
- Safety glasses
- Heatproof mat

1 Put the slide on a heatproof mat. Make sure that there are **no flames** in the laboratory.

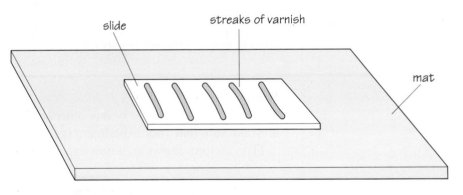

slide

streaks of varnish

mat

2 You can use the streaks of nail varnish to find out which solvent would make the best nail-varnish remover.
The drawing will help you to design your experiment.
Remember to keep it fair.

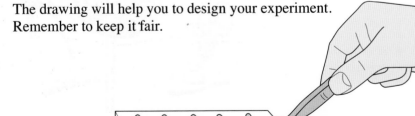

1 Describe your experiment and how you made it fair.
2 Make a table for your results.
3 Which solvent(s) would make good nail-varnish remover?

The Dead Sea

The Dead Sea is a warm sea. It is unusual because the water contains a large amount of dissolved substances. In fact the Dead Sea could be described as a huge volume of warm saturated solution.

1 **Explain** the appearance of the twigs in the second photograph.
2 Read about 'floating' in a reference book. Why do you think a person can float easily in the Dead Sea?
3 The Dead Sea contains different dissolved substances which have different properties. Read the graph below to find out
   a which substance is most soluble at 60°C?
   b which substance is most soluble at 20°C?
   c which substances are equally soluble at 34°C?
4 What happens to the solubility of the different substances as the temperature rises?

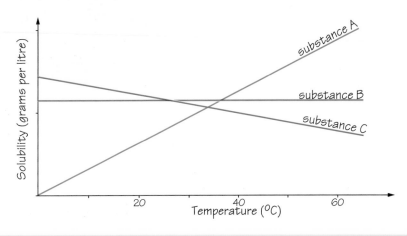

Be a rock star

Rocks are mixtures of minerals.
- **Igneous** rocks form as molten rock cools down. When this happens quickly they are made of small crystals. All igneous rocks are hard.
- **Sedimentary** rocks form in layers. They have few crystals and they can be quite soft.
- **Metamorphic** rocks form slowly when other rocks are heated and pushed together. They have crystals, sometimes large ones, and they are very hard.

Igneous (basalt)

Sedimentary (sandstone)

Metamorphic (hornfels)

Collect

- Samples of named rock
- Hand lens (or binocular microscope)
- Nail
- Geological hammer (if available)
- Safety glasses

Examine the sample and decide if it is a rock (mixture) or a mineral (single substance). Use the equipment to find out if the rock sample is igneous, sedimentary or metamorphic.

You will need to test for
- hardness
- presence and size of crystals.

Complete a report sheet like the following one.

Name	Hard?	Any crystals?	Size of crystal?	Rock or mineral? Type?
basalt	√	√	tiny	rock igneous

Orange perfume

The separating technique of **distillation** is used in the perfume industry. Many plants contain smelly oils which can be put into perfume. The oil is taken out by heating the plant material and distilling the vapour.

Collect

- Fresh orange peel
- Wire gauze basket
- Thread
- Bunsen burner and mat
- Tripod stand
- 2 flasks
- Condenser
- Safety glasses
- Ice
- Clamp stand

1 Quarter fill one flask with water.
2 Put the orange peel in the wire basket. Hang it above the water level with thread.
3 Finish setting up the apparatus as shown below.

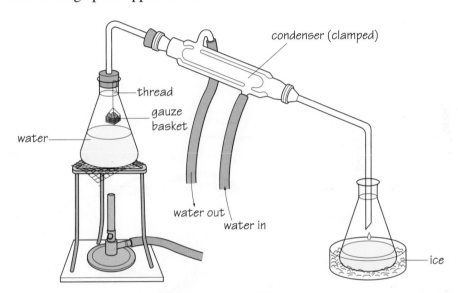

4 Heat the water **gently** to produce steam. The steam will take the oil out of the orange peel. Collect the oil for about two minutes. It should smell tremendously nice!

Write a full report about this experiment.
Include
- the method (description of what you did)
- a diagram
- a spot of perfumed oil in your book
- an explanation of how distillation works.

Signs of life

When the American Mariner probe landed on Mars it was able to test the Martian soil for living things. Unfortunately the experiments could not give very definite results and there was no astronaut present to carry out more detailed observations.

Imagine that you are Chuck L. Peyton Jnr, Astronaut 1st class. You have leapt down from the first manned Mars probe and just narrowly avoided stepping on a small squelchy thing.

1 Describe five simple observations that you could quickly make to indicate if the squelchy thing was a living thing.
2 Describe one longer test that you could do to indicate whether the squelchy thing is alive, dead or non-living. (Don't do anything that will kill it!)
3 How would you decide if the thing was an animal or a plant, assuming it turned out to be alive?

An eye for detail

Until recently, fungi (such as toadstools and mushrooms) and algae (such as seaweed) were classified as plants. Now they are in groups on their own.

Look closely at the drawings of the living things, or at the display.

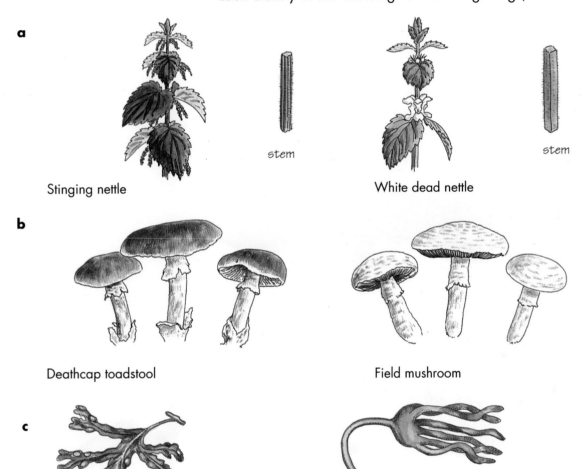

a

Stinging nettle   stem   White dead nettle   stem

b

Deathcap toadstool   Field mushroom

c

Bladder wrack   Kelp

1 What evidence is there that mushrooms and toadstools
   a are not flowering plants?
   b are not plants?

2 What evidence is there that the seaweeds (bladderwrack and kelp)
   a are not flowering plants?
   b are not plants?

3 What important details help you to tell the difference between the two **a** plants **b** fungi **c** algae?

Unusual mammals

You are going to brighten up your science laboratory. Your work will be displayed on the wall for all to see and admire.

1 Find out about **one** unusual mammal. Use the school library, local library or the books available in the classroom.
2 Display your information

- as a poster *or*
- as an information leaflet *or*
- in a sound or video report.

Hints
Use the index and contents pages of the books. Skim and scan any useful pages.

Making keys

You can begin to make a key by dividing the objects into two sets. One set will be different from the other in **one** important detail. These sets are then divided again and again until each object is in a set on its own.

For example, look at these pets.

Dog

Manx cat

Rabbit

Horse

1 Copy the table.
If the pet has the detail then put a tick in that box.

	Dog	Cat	Rabbit	Horse
Short tail				
Long tail				
Short ears				
Long ears				

2 Copy the branching key into your book.
Use the information from your table to complete the key.

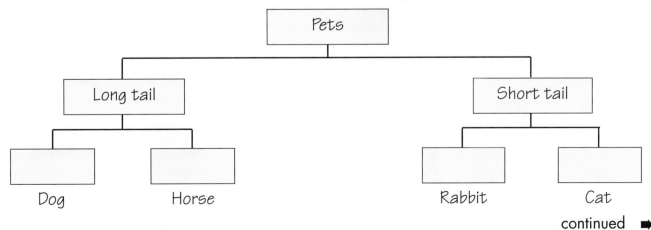

continued ➡

3 look at the pictures of rockpool fish.
Use the following clues to make a branching key.

Rockpool fish

two top fins

tail not divided

Armed bullhead

one top fin

Lesser weaver

Two-spotted sucker

barbels on head

divided tail

Sand eel

Bearded rockling

4 Look at the pictures of garden birds.
Making a branching key.

Garden birds

Robin

Chaffinch

Blue tit

Starling

Blackbird

House sparrow

5 Your teacher may allow you to make a class key. Here are some important details to look out for.

Left/right handed

Freckles

Tongue rolling

Cross hands

Sex

Hair type

Energy in store

There are three different types of stored energy: potential energy, nuclear energy and chemical energy.

Potential energy
is the type of
energy that a stone
has at the top of a
hill and . . .

Chemical energy
is the type of
energy that food
has and . . .

Nuclear energy
is the type of
energy used in
atomic explosions
and . . .

1 Write down three types of stored energy.
2 Copy and complete the table.

Types of stored energy	Two examples	
	a	b
	a	b
	a	b

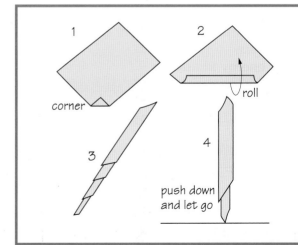

A piece of paper can be rolled diagonally to make a spring. This spring can store energy.

Use different sizes of the same kind of paper (half a sheet, quarter and so on) and find out
a if a small spring stores more energy than a large spring
b if a loose roll stores more energy than a tight roll.

Difficult energy transfers

Sometimes it is difficult to identify an energy transfer when something happens. This can be because

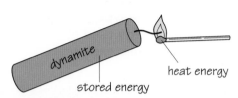

dynamite

heat energy

stored energy

- you start with more than one form of energy

heat energy
light energy
stored energy

- one of the forms is difficult to spot

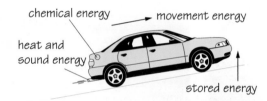

chemical energy → movement energy

heat and sound energy

stored energy

- the starting form of energy becomes another form and then another!

light energy

sound energy

heat energy

electrical energy

- many different energy transfers happen at once.

Do the following experiments.

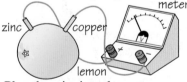

meter

zinc   copper

lemon

a Plug the wire into the meter.

b Dip the wire in the chemical. Hold it in the flame.

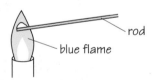

rod

blue flame

thermometer

c Hold the thermometer across your forehead. Look in a mirror.

---

1 Write a report about **one** of your experiments. Your report should be like the description of the Bunsen burner on page 44. Include **all** the energy transfers.

2 Identify the most important energy transfer in

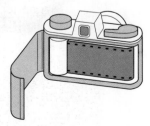

a a growing plant   **b** a moving helicopter   **c** a film in a camera   **d** a lighted candle

Machines that go on forever

A machine transfers one form of energy into other forms. All machines 'waste' some of the energy that they start with.

A car transfers stored energy into movement energy when it starts up and when it is running. Yet a lot of the stored energy from the fuel is wasted. It is lost mainly as unused heat energy and some sound energy.

Go to one of the machines in the room and make it work.

1 Write a report about one of the machines. Draw an energy account for the machine. Colour the wasted (unused) energy in red.

2 Explain why the machine eventually stops.

3 Look at the picture below.
Is energy wasted in this water wheel or can it go on forever? Explain your answer.

4.4 Extension

Photosynthesis

Photosynthesis is important for many reasons. Green plants make food (sugar and starch) by photosynthesis. They also make oxygen gas. Animals use up the oxygen gas. They also eat the food that the plant makes.

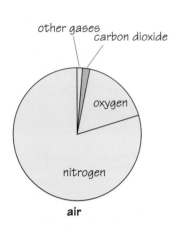

Photosynthesis helps keep the balance of gases in the air

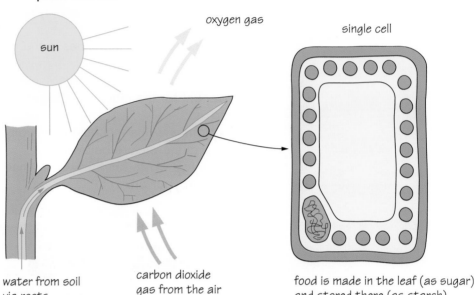

water from soil via roots

carbon dioxide gas from the air

food is made in the leaf (as sugar) and stored there (as starch)

Collect

- Water plant
- Bench lamp
- Metre rule
- Timer
- Paperclip

Water plants use light energy to make food and oxygen. You can count the oxygen bubbles produced.

1 Examine this drawing of an experiment.
2 Design and carry out an experiment to test fairly whether or not photosynthesis speeds up as the light gets stronger.

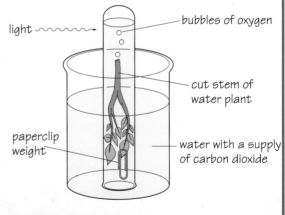

1 Write a report about your investigation describing
  - your experiment and results
  - what you found out.
2 Copy and complete this sentence.

In photosynthesis the plant uses _____ energy to change water and _____ gas into _____ gas and (glucose) sugar.

114

Energy from substances

Oxygen is a gas. It is found in the air. Oxygen helps your body get energy from food (**respiration**). Oxygen is also needed to get fuels to burn and release energy (**combustion**).

Respiration

Combustion

Collect

- Test tube of oxygen
- Wood splint
- Bunsen burner and mat
- Equipment for each experiment
- Safety glasses

1 **The combustion test for oxygen**
   a Light a wooden splint.
   b Blow it out.
   c Put the **glowing** splint just inside the test tube. Observe what happens to the end of the splint. This is the test for oxygen.

2 Use the combustion test to find out which of these experiments produces oxygen.

hydrogen peroxide

potatoes

1 In what ways are respiration and combustion similar?
2 How do you test for oxygen? What happens?
3 Write a short report about the experiments you did.

Useful properties of metals

Metals are useful because they can be

- made into wires

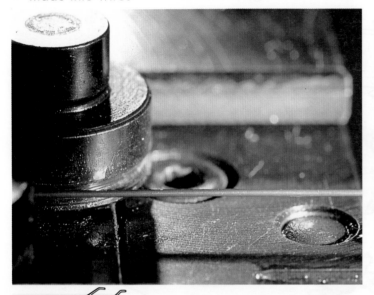

- bent and shaped

You have been hired to design a TV transmission tower. It has two main parts – a rigid metal tower and metal wires to support the tower. Which of the available metals should you use?

1 Study the diagram. It suggests a way of comparing the strength of metal wires.

2 Study the diagram. It suggests a way of changing the shape of metal strips.

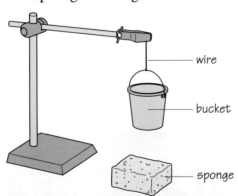

wire

bucket

sponge

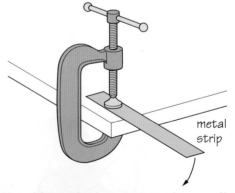

metal strip

Design and do an experiment which compares the strength of the wires. Make sure that your comparison is **fair**.

Use this method to compare how well the strips keep their shape. Make sure that your comparison is **fair**.

Report your findings to the Directors of the TV company. Include

a a drawing of your experiments

b labels to explain how you made the comparison fair

c a table/bar graph of your results.

Metals and non-metals

Metals are used throughout a modern home. See how many examples you can spot in this cartoon.

Metal elements are on the left-hand side of the periodic table. They are all solids at room temperature, except mercury. The 21 non-metallic elements are on the right-hand side. Only nine are solids at room temperature: many are gases.

Collect

- Tray containing solid elements (labelled A, B, C, D, E, F and G)
- Anything else you need to do the tests

1 Divide the elements into two sets by appearance **only**.

2 Think about the properties of a typical metal (pages 56–57)
Carry out tests to find out which elements are metals and which are non-metals.
For each test write down your results.

1 Describe these properties of the metal group: appearance, conduction of electricity and heat, and strength.
2 Describe the same properties of the non-metallic group. (*Be careful:* there is at least one unexpected result in this group.)
3 Use a reference book or a poster to identify each element.

Electroplating

Electricity can be used to break up a compound into separate elements. The metal element can then be attracted to an object so that it forms a metallic coat. This is known as **electroplating.**

These objects have been electroplated

Collect

- Materials to build circuit
- Copper coin and nickel sulphate solution *or* silver coin and copper sulphate solution
- Safety glasses

How to electroplate a coin

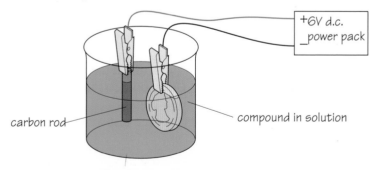

+6V d.c. power pack

carbon rod

compound in solution

1 Set up the circuit.
Use copper sulphate solution in the beaker if you have a 'silver' coin.
Use nickel sulphate solution in the beaker if you have a 'copper' coin.
2 Make sure that the coin is the negative terminal.
3 Switch on and leave for a few minutes.

 Describe the experiment. Use a labelled diagram to explain where the metal coat on the coin comes from.

Electric charge on the move

The charging of an object with electricity can be explained by the movement of electrons. **Electrons** are tiny and carry a *negative* electric charge. When polythene is charged by rubbing it with a cloth, electrons move from the cloth to the polythene. This gives the polythene a negative charge (because it has gained electrons) and the cloth a positive charge (because it has lost electrons).

I HAVE LOST ELECTRONS

I HAVE GAINED ELECTRONS

Collect

- Van de Graaff machine
- Thread
- Ammeter
- Connecting wire

In this experiment, electrons are forced to move down a thread.

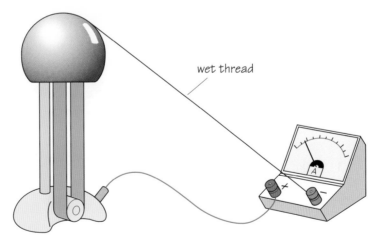

wet thread

1 Connect a thread from the dome of a Van de Graaff machine to a very sensitive ammeter (ammeters measure electric current).
2 Complete the circuit with a wire from the ammeter to the base of the generator.
3 Turn the belt for a while and charge up the dome of the generator. Watch carefully what happens.

1 Describe carefully what happens to the ammeter from the moment you start to turn the belt until it stops again.
2 Do your observations fit in with the idea that electric charge can move?
   Explain your answer carefully.

Symbol for a voltmeter

Batteries

A battery contains chemicals which store energy. When you use a battery the stored energy is transferred and becomes electrical energy. The main energy transfer is

stored (chemical) → electrical

Collect

- 5p coin
- 2p coin
- Wire
- Voltmeter
- 2 wires
- 2 pieces of metal
- Orange
- Set of metals
- Beaker of vinegar

1 Wash a 5p coin and a 2p coin. Join the coins with a wire. Hold them apart on your tongue.

2 **Collect** a voltmeter and two wires. Attach a wire to each piece of metal. Stick the pieces of metal into the orange. Note the reading on the voltmeter.

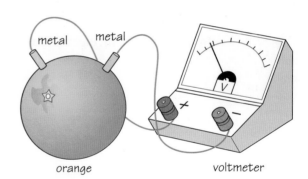

orange   voltmeter

3 Make this model battery.

Find out which pair of metals gives the highest reading on the voltmeter.

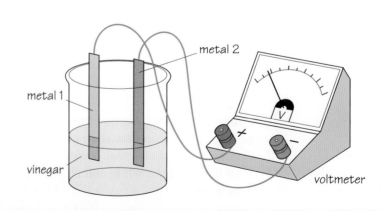

metal 1

metal 2

vinegar

voltmeter

1 Describe what happened in experiment **1**.
2 Draw the diagram for experiment **2**. What was the voltmeter reading?
3 Write a report about experiment **3**. Include a diagram, a description of the method and the result in a suitable form.

Big potential difference

Measuring potential difference

Electrical energy is transferred into other forms of energy by the components of an electric circuit. A bulb transfers electrical energy into heat and light energy. A buzzer transfers electrical energy into sound energy.

The **potential difference** across a component is the amount of energy transferred by a unit of charge. Potential difference is often called voltage and is measured in volts.

Collect

- Electrical components
- Voltmeter (WARNING be sure to connect the voltmeter correctly – see page 68)

1 Build circuits A and B.

Circuit A

Circuit B

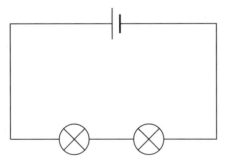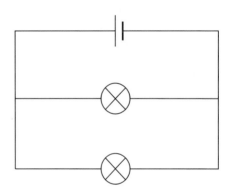

2 Use the voltmeter to measure the potential difference across each bulb in:
- circuit A
- circuit B.

1 Write a report on both circuits. You should include:
- a circuit diagram, showing the voltmeter in place across one of the components
- a description of the circuit in words
- a table showing the potential difference in volts across each bulb
- a rule to link the potential difference across the battery with the potential differences elsewhere in the circuit.

2 Use your result to **explain** why the bulbs in one circuit are brighter than the bulbs in the other circuit.

Upstairs/downstairs

If there are stairs in your house then you need two switches to control the stair light—one upstairs and one downstairs. This problem can be solved by using 2 two-way switches.

Collect

- Bulb
- 2 batteries
- 6 wires
- Drawing pins
- Paper-clips
- Blocks of wood

Try to design switches and build a circuit which will switch one light on and off from two different switches.

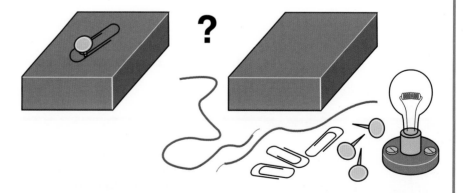

When the circuit is working show it to your teacher.

1 Make a drawing of your two-way switch.
2 Draw a circuit diagram of your circuit.
3 **Explain** how your circuit works.

Using electricity

Many living things use electricity. Here are some examples.

1 Some fish can generate electricity in their bodies to find their way about in murky water. Special muscles send out small electrical signals which are used for navigation.

2 There is a lot of electrical activity in animal brains including your own. This EEG (electroencephalograph) traces the electrical activity in a human brain.

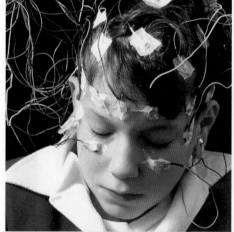
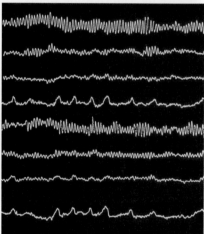

3 There is also electrical activity in the heart. When the heart muscle contracts the heartbeat is accompanied by electrical changes. We can measure these using an ECG (electrocardiogram). This is a trace from an ECG.

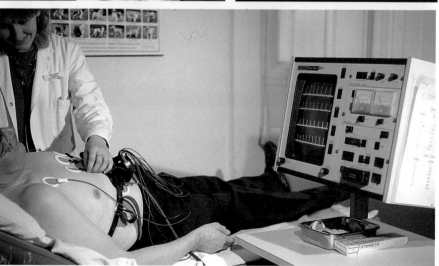

continued ➡

4 Electricity can be used to repair faults in the body.

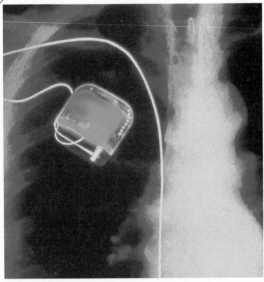

A faulty heart can be controlled by an artificial pacemaker which uses electricity to make the heart beat at the correct rate.

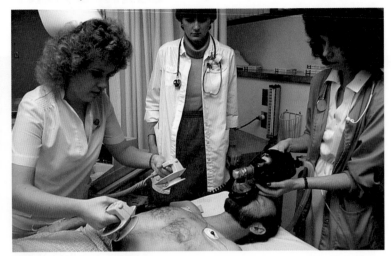

A heart which stops can be restarted by giving it an electric shock.

The cardiac arrest team must stand back from the patient while a large voltage is applied to the chest.

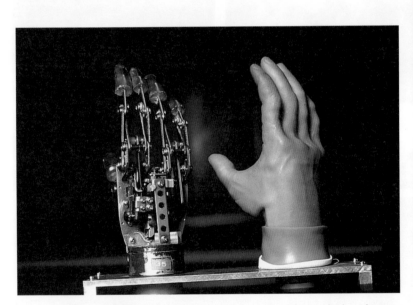

An artificial limb can be controlled by a little electric motor. The motor is switched on and off by muscle contractions in the limb stump.

1 Write a short paragraph about electricity in living creatures.
2 Write a short paragraph about the use of electricity in medicine.

Flea in your eye

This is an outline of the body shape of a water flea (called *Daphnia*).

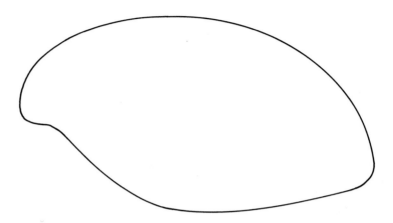

A water flea is tiny and you need a microscope to see the important body parts. The following parts are missing from the drawing above: legs, antennae, heart, eye and long gut tube.

Collect

• Water flea
• Slide

1 Copy the outline of the water flea.
2 Put a water flea on a slide. Make sure the animal is in a drop of water.

3 Focus the microscope on the water flea. Find the

• legs
• heart
• eyes
• long gut tube
• antennae.

4 Add the important body parts to your outline shape. Label them.
5 Return the water flea to its container.
6 Have a look for other animals in the pondwater that is available. Draw any animal or plant that you see.

Living cells

All living cells make a chemical that causes bubbles in hydrogen peroxide solution. The bubbles, which contain oxygen gas, show clearly at low magnification with a hand lens. So hydrogen peroxide can be used to test for **living** cells.

Collect

- Dropper bottle of hydrogen peroxide solution
- Small bits of your hair, nail and dandruff
- Small bits of potato, carrot, fresh meat and celery
- Safety glasses
- Slide and cover slip

Test each sample as follows:

1 Make a slide of the substance.

2 Add **one drop** of hydrogen peroxide solution. Cover with a cover slip.

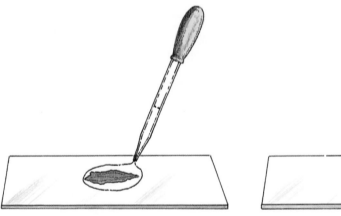

3 Focus the hand lens on the slide and look first for cells and then for bubbles. Is the sample cellular (made of cells)? Are the cells alive?

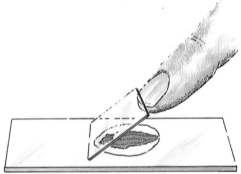

 Write a report about your experiment.

Structure and function

In living things structure is always related to function. The pollen grains of flowering plants are a good example. Although pollen is microscopic, it is made of many cells. Pollen contains the male sex cell which is passed from one flower to another during reproduction. This can happen in one of two ways:

- pollen carried in the wind
- pollen carried by an insect by sticking to the insect's body.

The structure of a pollen grain helps it to move by blowing in the wind or by sticking to an insect. Pollen from two different flowering plants are shown below. How are they carried?

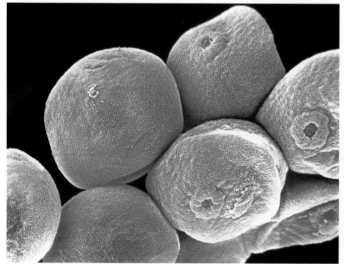

Pollen from a grass

Pollen from a hollyhock flower

Collect

- Prepared slides A and B

1 Examine each slide. Look closely at, and compare the structures of the pollen. Look for differences in

  - size
  - appearance of surface
  - shape
  - number of pollen grains.

2 Make a large drawing of one pollen grain from each slide. Add a few words under your drawing to describe the structure of each grain.

3 Label one grain 'Carried by wind'. Label the other grain 'Carried by an insect'.

1 Write down the names of three plants that depend on wind to carry their pollen. What structures might their pollen grains have in common?

2 Write down the names of three plants that depend on insects to carry their pollen. What structures might their pollen grains have in common?

Health and efficiency

There are many variations on the basic pattern of reproduction within the animal kingdom. Reproduction is efficient when there is a good chance of an egg being fertilised, and a good chance of this developing, then growing to maturity. Three factors affect the efficiency of reproduction:

- **Type of fertilisation**
  External fertilisation takes place outside the body of the female.
  Internal fertilisation takes place within the body of the female.

- **Where the embryo grows**
  Outside the female's body.
  Inside the female's body.

- **Amount of parental care**
  No or low amount of parental care.
  High amount of parental care.

Find out about how these three factors affect the efficiency of reproduction in the following:

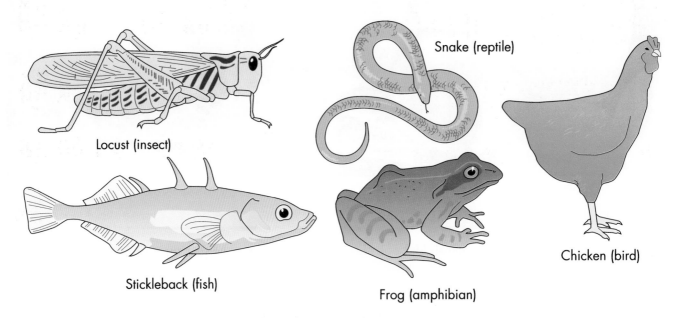

Snake (reptile)

Locust (insect)

Chicken (bird)

Stickleback (fish)

Frog (amphibian)

Can you arrange these examples of reproduction from least efficient to most efficient? (Use the information in Topic 7.4 A and B and in books available in the classroom or library to help.)

1 **Collect** and complete a summary table.
2 Where would you put humans in your summary table? Explain your answer.
3 Do animals that reproduce efficiently produce many or few eggs at a time? Why do you think this is?

Messages in cells

The plan for your body is inside the nucleus of each of your cells. People look different mainly because their plans are different.

The plan is in the form of a chemical code. The code is carried by a chemical called **DNA.**

The code is made up of small bits called **genes**, rather like this sentence is made up of bits called words. Each gene contains one part of the plan for your body. There are genes for hair colour, blood group and so on.

A single length of DNA is called a **chromosome** and it contains thousands of genes. When cells are dividing you can sometimes see the chromosomes through a microscope.

The chromosomes are all jumbled up in the cell. However we draw them like this.

Human female chromosomes

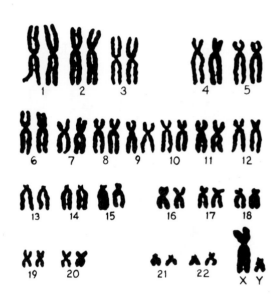

Human male chromosomes

1 Why do people look different?
2 What is a chromosome?
3 How many chromosomes are in the human chromosome set?
4 Look at the picture of the human male chromosome set. How is it different from the female chromosome set?
5 What information do you think is on the Y chromosome?

Seed dispersal

After fertilisation the ovary wall becomes a fruit. The ovules inside the ovary become seeds. Seeds have to be spread away from the parent plant to give them a better chance to grow well. Plants disperse their seeds in different ways.

| Blown in the wind | Eaten or partly eaten | Carried on an animal | Thrown by explosion |

parachute of hairs

Dandelion

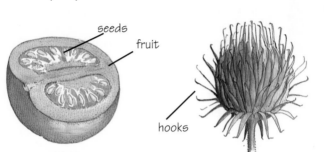

seeds

fruit

Tomato

hooks

Burdock

seed is ejected

Geranium

1 Look at the pictures above. What useful structures help each seed to be dispersed in the way described?

2 Here is a picture of a seed and fruit collection. You may have a bigger collection in class.

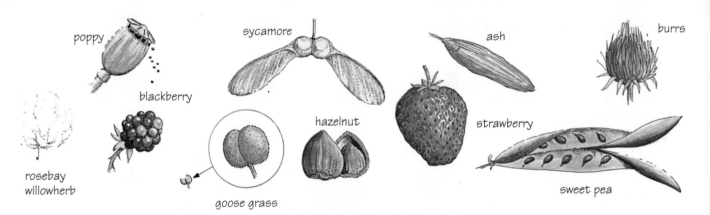

poppy

blackberry

rosebay willowherb

goose grass

sycamore

hazelnut

strawberry

ash

burrs

sweet pea

Copy and complete this table to show how each set of seeds is dispersed.

	Blown in the wind	Eaten or partly eaten	Carried on an animal	Thrown by explosion
Useful structures				
Examples				

Index

Acknowledgements

Cover photo: ZEFA

The following have provided photographs or given permission for photographs to be reproduced:

p.v *from top to bottom* Blair Seitz/Science Photo Library; ZEFA; NHPA; Rex Features

p.vi *top* ZEFA; *middle* Peter Menzel/Science Photo Library; *bottom* NHPA

p.vii Will and Deni McIntyre/Science Photo Library

p.1 Blair Seitz/Science Photo Library

p.3 *all photos* Tom Harrison

p.13 *top left* Peter Menzel/Science Photo Library; *top right* Pacific Press Service/Science Photo Library; *bottom left* Rex Features; *bottom right* Rex Features

p.14 Mary Evans Picture Library

p.15 ZEFA

p.21 *top left* Rex Features; *top right* GSF Picture Library; *bottom left* GSF Picture Library; *bottom right* NHPA

p.26 *top left and right* John Townson/Creation; *bottom* Rex Features

p.27 *top* Rex Features; *bottom* Planet Earth Pictures

p.28 G. Garvey/Ancient Art and Architecture Collection

p.29 NHPA

p.31 *top left* Planet Earth Pictures; *top right* Dr Jeremy Burgess/Science Photo Library; *bottom left* NHPA; *bottom right* ZEFA

p.39 *top right* Roger Ressmeyer, Starlight/Science Photo Library; *bottom left* Rex Features; *bottom right* David Hardy/Science Photo Library

p.40 National Library of Medicine/Science Photo Library

p.41 Rex Features

p.47 *top far left* Rex Features; *far left* Allsport/Image Select; *middle* NASA/Science Photo Library; *right* Tom McHugh/Science Photo Library

p.50 Discovery of electricity – *top* Instituion of Electrical Engineers; *bottom* Image Select. Making electricity *top* Rex Features; *bottom* John Walsh/Science Photo Library. Working with electricity – ZEFA. Using electricity sensibly – British Standards Institute.

p.52 *left* Hulton Deutsch; *right* Ronald Sheridan/Ancient Art and Architecture Collection

p.53 ZEFA

p.55 *top left* NASA/Science Photo Library; *top right* Last Resort Picture Library; *bottom left* Rex Features; *bottom right* John Howard/Science   Photo Library

p.56 Ronald Sheridan/Ancient Art and Architecture Collection

p.58 *potassium, sodium, magnesium, iron* GSF Picture Library; *titanium, chromium* Russ Lappa/Science Photo Library

p.59 *carbon, silicon, bromine* GSF Picture Library; *sulphur* Sidney Moulds/Science Photo Library; *iodine* Claude Nuridsany and Marie Perennon/Science Photo Library

p.63 *left* Rex Features; *top right* ZEFA; *bottom right* Rex Features

p.64 Novosti/Science Photo Library

p.65 Peter Menzel/Science Photo Library

p.73 *left* Megger Instruments; *right* David Purdie

p.77 *top left* ZEFA; *top right* Rex Features; *middle left* Rex Features; *bottom left* Hank Morgan/Science Photo Library; *bottom right* Rex Features

p.78 Schomburg Center for Research in Black Culture, NY, USA

p.79 NHPA

p.80 *far left* Larry Mulvehill/Science Photo Library; *inset left* John Burbidge/Science Photo Library; *right* Philippe Platilly/Eurelios/Science Photo Library; *inset right* David Scharf/Science Photo Library; *bottom* Griffin & George

p.84 GSF Picture Library

p.85 Francis Leroy, Biocosmos/Science Photo Library

p.94 The Natural History Museum, London

p.95 Will and Deni McIntyre/Science Photo Library

p.99 Rex Features

p.101 *all photos* John Townson/Creation

p.103 *left* Rex Features; *right* NHPA

p.104 *left* Rex Features; *middle* Astrid and Hans-Frieder Michler/Science Photo   Library; *right* GSF Picture Library

p.105 John Townson/Creation

p.111 *left and middle* Rex Features; *right* Martin Bond/Science Photo Library

p.113 © 1995 M.C. Escher/Cordon Art – Baarn – Holland. All rights reserved.

p.116 *left* Philippe Platilly/Eurelios/Science Photo Library; *right* NHPA

p.118 *both photos* ZEFA

p.121 Johnny Autrey/Science Photo Library

p.123 *top* Planet Earth Pictures; *middle left* Alexander Tsiaras/Science Photo Library; *middle right and bottom* Science Photo Library

p.124 *top left* BSIP VEM/Science Photo Library; *top right* Grapes/Michand/Science Photo Library; *bottom left* Claude Charlier/Science Photo Library; *bottom right* Rex Features

p.127 *left* CNRI/Science Photo Library; *right* Andrew Syred/Science Photo Library

p.129 ZEFA